ASLEEP AT THE WHEEL: A LIFELONG STRUGGLE WITH NARCOLEPSY

Jeffrey J. Wood

ISBN-13: 978-0-692-19111-8

*This book is dedicated to the memories of
My son, Jeffrey Stephen Wood,
my brother William Raymond Wood the II,
And my little buddy Hunter Bear.
Sherry Ann Wood
I miss you guys.*

CONTENTS

CHAPTER 1

ASLEEP AT THE WHEEL

I t was November 2009, and I was in my room at the National Institute of Health. The study nurse had just walked in to give me my discharge instructions—I had just finished a three-week research study as a patient with narcolepsy.

The nurse asked me if I ever felt like I was in a movie. I said, "Yes, as a matter of fact, I have."

I proceeded to tell her about an incident that occurred around 1992. I was in my early twenties. A jogger was passing by my vehicle one Saturday morning. He suddenly noticed I was asleep in my vehicle. He stopped to reach through the driver's window to shake me, and he shouted, "Hey, buddy, are you okay?"

"Yeah, yeah, I'm okay," I answered. However, I didn't know where I was or how I got there. Apparently, I had spent the night in my car on a side street in Royal Oak, Michigan, with the car running and the windows down, when the jogger woke me up.

After I was alert and functioning better, I remembered the night before was Friday night and I had stopped by my friend's house. He told me I had left around nine o'clock that evening—the jogger woke me up around seven the next morning. That left about ten hours that were unaccounted for. I was only about two miles from my friend's house when that jogger woke me up, so I assume that I went nowhere else that night. Luckily, it was summer, and I had all the windows down. I hadn't been drinking or anything like that the night before.

This was not the first time (and it was far from the last time) that something like this would occur. Many times strange things like this would happen throughout my childhood and adult years.

CHAPTER 2

SAILBOAT

One early Sunday afternoon in the summer of 1989, two of my friends and I headed to a metro Detroit area lake to meet family and friends for a lakeside cookout. My brother had called me earlier that morning and told me not to forget our family's aluminum fishing boat. I thought that sounded good: it had been a while since we had gotten some bass fishing in. My friends Nick and John showed up at my house around noon that day. "Nick," I said, "why don't you guys give me a hand throwing the flat-bottom boat on top of my Oldsmobile?

Nick and John pitched in and grabbed the boat from my garage and hoisted it up on to my car.

I was in charge of tying the boat down. I gathered up some rope from the garage and began fastening the boat down securely. I remember tying the sides down first, and then I ran back into the garage to get my fishing gear so I wouldn't forget it. "Nick, John," I yelled, "grab your coolers and stuff, and throw them in the trunk—we can all drive out together."

We loaded up the car, and then I finished tying the boat down. I slid the oars in on the side of the boat snugly by the side tie-downs. I hopped in the driver's seat as Nick slipped into the passenger seat and John hopped in the back. I asked, "Are you guys ready to go?"

They replied, "We're ready!"

John asked me, "Do you have the boat all tied down?"

I replied, "Yep, good to go."

We headed up M-24 through the heart of northern Oakland County, Michigan. We stopped at a red light right near the Palace of Auburn Hills where the Detroit Pistons basketball team played. I said, "Look, the Palace."

Nick replied, "Yeah, I see it. So what?"

Then I responded, "I helped build that."

John chimed in, "That's right; you did."

"I'm surprised it is still standing," added Nick.

"Very funny," I replied.

The red light changed, and we headed up the road a little way further; as luck would have it, we caught the next red light too.

I remember it was a very hot summer day and we had all the windows down. In the lane next to us, the driver had his window down too. He was shouting something to me; I couldn't hear him, so I turned the radio down and yelled, "What?"

The driver shouted again, and this time I thought I heard him clearly: "Are you going to sail the boat?"

I said, "No, we are going to row it."

Just then, Nick hit me in the shoulder and said, "No, you idiot, he wants to know if you want to sell the boat."

I yelled across to the driver of the other car, "I'm sorry, man. No, not selling. I want to keep it, but thanks for asking."

The driver yelled, "Okay, have fun."

I said, "Thanks!"

The light changed, and we headed up the road again to the lake.

About a mile or so up the road, we started up a hill. I remember looking through the windshield of the car at the front of the boat. The boat seemed to jump up a little, and then all of a sudden, the front rope broke. I couldn't believe it; I watched the boat from the rearview mirror, flying in the air like a kite. The oars were spinning through the air like helicopters. I turned and looked behind the car while we were still driving; in horror all I could think was I just killed someone. I watched the boat hit the pavement like an airplane, cars swerving out of the way like an accident from a movie. Just then Nick yelled, "Jeff, look out!" My car was in the ditch on the side of the road. We spun around a few times; I was able to get the car to come to a stop without too much incident and with no one getting hurt.

At that point I realized the cars behind us made it through untouched, but I needed to get the boat off the highway before another car hit it. Luckily two people from a house nearby pulled the boat and oars from the road. I was so relieved; nobody was hurt. The only damage was to the boat and oars. I must have had an angel looking out for me that day.

I talked to the residents from the house who pulled the boat off the road. I thanked them. They told me they were glad to help and things like that happen there all the time. Nick, John, and I put the boat back on the car; this time they double-checked my work. We decided to continue our trip to the lake; after all, we were almost there anyway.

Once in the car, Nick said, "The guy we had met earlier at the red light was right after all, Jeff. You did 'sail' the boat."

I said, "Very funny, Nick." At that point I didn't even care I was the butt of the joke. I was just happy that everyone was okay.

When we arrived at the lake, the three of us unpacked the boat and the rest of the car. We put the boat in the water, and you could really see it the aluminum boat had a heck of a bend to it. However the boat was still usable. In the water the boat looked like it was always making a right turn; it was a sight to see. I remember we kept the boat for years after that. One day, however, someone stole the boat from behind my family cabin in northern Michigan. When it happened, my older brother mentioned if we ever see that boat in a lake one day, we will know it is ours. We both laughed. I am not sure, but the whole boat incident probably had something to do with my narcolepsy and lack of alertness at the time.

CHAPTER 3

FLY WHEEL

One Saturday evening in 1994, my friend Craig and I headed up to a local bar to check out the band. We drove my vehicle, and as we headed to the bar, my car was making a weird sound from the front end. We arrived at the bar; it was only a few miles from our homes. We ordered drinks and sat down to check out the band. I was worried about my vehicle, so I called Kurt, who was a guy that I knew was very knowledgeable about cars. I explained what was going on and that my car was making a weird noise. He told me that it was probably the brakes and he would check it out in the morning, which sounded good to me. Craig and I watched a couple of bands play their sets, and then we decided to head home.

My car was still making the strange noise. A couple of miles later, about half way home from the bar, I entered an intersection. Suddenly, I heard a loud noise and felt a jolt in the front end. My driver's side wheel flew off the car. The momentum of the car pulled itself and us into the gas-station parking lot, where I watched the car wheel bounce through a window wall. Although there was shattered glass everywhere, no one was hurt.

The police were called to the scene, and I was quite worried. The police officer asked for my identification, and I quickly gave it to him. As he was looking at my license and registration, I remembered that I had a bow and arrow in my back seat from when I was target practicing earlier in the day. The bow was not in a case, and I knew I could get a ticket for that. The officer noticed the uncased bow and mentioned he was a bow hunter also. He didn't seem to care it wasn't in a case, so I relaxed about it.

The police officer continued to fill out his police report. He mentioned that it looked like someone was trying to kill me and the person loosened up my wheel. That was scary—I hadn't thought of that. The officer announced he would finish his report and then I could be on my way, and I wouldn't be getting a ticket. That was good news for me.

As the officer started to walk the scene so he could draw it up for his report, he asked me where the wheel had started to come off. I told him that it had happened right in the middle of the intersection. He walked out to check the skid marks and came back with some bad news. I said, "What's wrong?"

He replied, "The wheel actually came off the car in the neighboring city and bounced into this one."

"Now what?" I said. The officer told me he had to call the other city's police out, as it was their jurisdiction.

Two officers from the neighboring city arrived about five minutes later, and they were not as nice as the first one. Fortunately, I still avoided a ticket. They filled out the report. I put the wheel back on and went on my way.

I still don't know to this day if someone loosened up my wheel or if it was my fault. Many odd things happened to me similar to this before and after that day.

CHAPTER 4

WE ARE TAKING YOUR BLOOD

It was November 1996, and I was right in the middle of
Michigan's Upper Peninsula at one of my favorite times of
the year: deer-hunting season. As Jeff Daniels famously said
in the movie *Escanaba in Da Moonlight*, "it's like Christmas
with guns!"[1] Need I say more? This season was shaping up
to be the best one yet. Hunting camps had never been so
full. Over twenty people, family and friends, were packed
into the three small cabins, tents, and trailers that scattered
across the twenty-five-acre hunting camp that my four brothers and I shared in a remote spot between Manistique and
Escanaba, Michigan. Most were there for hunting, some to

---

1 *Escanaba in Da Moonlight*, directed by Jeff Daniels, United States:
Purple Rose Films, 2001.

get away from the city and the rat race, but all were there to have a good time.

Usually, hunting camps would start to populate a week or so before the opening day of the hunting season, which, in Michigan, is always November 15. Throughout that week, more and more hunters and partiers would show up, until November 14, the eve of the opener, when all the rest would pile in. Daniels was right. All of us adults had the same feeling on the evening of November 14 as we did as kids on Christmas Eve—that feeling you just can't describe with words. At around 9:00 p.m., everyone in the camp was putting the final touches on whatever he or she needed to make the hunting season great. Some were packing lunches to stay out all day; others were in the woods on a road ride. Others still were celebrating and toasting with a beer or shot, whatever their drink of choice was. Myself? I was wiped out, and all I wanted to do was get to bed and get up early. My friend Tom had other plans.

"Come on, sonny. Let's head to town and check out the bands at the bars. You know it is going to be happening."

I replied, "I don't really feel like it tonight."

Tom made me feel guilty and reminded me that if I was at his hunting camp, he would take me out and show me a good time. I gave in, and Tom, my friend Craig, and I hopped in my car and headed to town.

It was around 11:00 p.m. when we arrived at the first bar. Things were going good, the band was rocking out, and everyone was having a good time. I had a beer, but I just wanted one—I was being careful because I knew I had to drive. About an hour passed by, and we met a couple of friends we knew and decided to leave with them to another bar.

This bar was right at the edge of town; from there, the two-lane highway headed for miles into the woods and very rural areas. I recall that we ordered a large pizza, and everyone had a few more drinks. I had one more beer but didn't even finish it. I know what you're thinking—that is like saying "I hit a joint but didn't inhale." I get it—I should never drink even *one* beer and drive, but having said that, I was being careful. We listened to some music and played some pool, and then before we knew it, it was time to go. The two lady friends we met at the bar asked if we could give them a ride home, and we happily obliged.

The five of us headed down the highway into the woods with me at the wheel. I noticed a vehicle behind us as we traveled west bound. Cindy, the lady in the front seat, lived closest, so we decided to take her home first. I told her to let me know when to turn. Just then she yelled, "Right here! Turn right here!"

I turned, but it wasn't the smoothest of turns. I did not have time to signal, and I took the turn kind of wild. Cindy apologized for not giving me advanced notice of where her street was.

The vehicle behind us followed with flashers and sirens, and I pulled over on the shoulder right away. It was a state police car with two officers. They approached one on each side. I rolled my window down and heard the voice of a lady asking me for my license, registration, and proof of insurance.

I fumbled around and handed the officer my paperwork. She asked, "Do you know why I pulled you over?"

I said, "I'm not sure."

She replied, "That was kind of a wild turn you made back there, Mr. Wood."

"Yeah, I know; sorry," I replied.

Just then the officer noticed she recognized the passenger in the front seat. She said, "Hi, Cindy!" I wasn't sure if that was good news or bad news.

The officer asked me to step out of the vehicle and asked if I had been drinking. I informed her I had about two beers. She then asked if I would mind performing a road sobriety test. I agreed.

First, they did the toe to toe (that is one of my favorites). Next they did the touch your nose and touch your toes. I felt I did well. Next, I was to recite my ABCs. I sang them perfectly, and then the other officer said, "You're not supposed to sing them!"

I told him that is the only way I know how to do it—that is how my kindergarten teacher, Mrs. Chapman, taught me. He might have thought I was being a smart-ass, but I was serious. For the next test, I was to follow the lady officer's finger back and forth. Then I was to follow her little light back and forth.

When those two tests were done, she commented, "You have quite a horizontal gaze."

I thought, *Okay, whatever that means.*

At this time, she decided to give me a breathalyzer test. She said, "When I say go, blow into the stem as hard as you can."

I did—I blew very hard. Just then, the male officer (Officer Duggan) said, "He is not blowing hard enough."

The female officer (Officer Macon) suggested I try again. I agreed, and this time, I blew with all my might—I felt like the wolf trying to blow down the three little pigs' brick house. Again officer Duggan cried, "He isn't blowing hard enough."

At that moment, I looked over at the breathalyzer, and it read ".04." About this time, I was wondering if they were going to write me a ticket or if we could be on our way. Officer Macon looked at me and said, "Your eyes are pretty red!"

"Thank you," I said with a smirk. "Yours are pretty blue."

She then informed me I was going to the police station, and I better blow harder there. At that point, they asked my friend Craig if he would perform a breathalyzer test to see if he could drive my car and take all the passengers home. The police assured him he had nothing to lose if he didn't pass the test—all it would mean was he wouldn't be able to drive my car.

Craig passed the test, and they let him drive my car. At least I wouldn't get my vehicle impounded—that was good news. Officer Macon handcuffed me and put me in the back seat as Officer Duggan reminded me that I better blow harder at the station. I then mentioned, "Hey, didn't that breath test say .04?"

Officer Macon then informed me that she didn't know what I was on, but I was on something, and they were going to take my blood and test it.

"Really," I said. "You can do that?"

"Of course we can," she said. "By the way, the blood test checks for THC and other indicators of drug use.

I replied, "Whatever. I don't smoke weed, and I don't do drugs."

We arrived at the police headquarters somewhere around 3:00 a.m. I blew once into the breathalyzer, and then one of the officers said, "Take him to the hospital." I was loaded up in the back of the police car again and shipped to the hospital. We were only at the hospital for about five minutes. I didn't fight the nurse; I let her take my blood. I don't remember if they said they had a warrant or anything, or if they even needed one. One thing is for sure: that was my fastest experience with a hospital before or since that night. That does make me wonder if we had a national health-care system in America, would it be a lot faster without miles of paperwork, and if so, would it be a lot cheaper?

I swear it was only another ten minutes or so, and I was fingerprinted, smiled for the camera, and tucked in for the night in a nice cold cell. I was the only one in there at the time (at least in my area of the jail), but at 3:00 a.m., I guess it was still early for a Saturday night. Things were about to get busier.

I remember it was 3:45 a.m. when I asked what time it was to the officer who escorted my new neighbor into the cell next to me. I thought, *Hey, at least I have company.* He seemed like a nice guy and introduced himself right away. He said, "I'm Tim."

I replied, "I'm Jeff."

He asked me what I was there for—I guess that is the first question everyone asks when you spend a night in jail. I said, "I am in for drunk driving."

"Really? You don't look drunk," he said.

I said, "Thanks. You're the only one here who thinks that."

I proceeded to tell him my story of the evening and how I got there.

"That's bull," he said.

"I think so too, but what are you gonna do?"

Now, it was my turn. I said, "Well, Tim, what are you in here for?"

"A domestic dispute," he said. Tim proceeded to tell me his story. He mentioned that he and his wife were having an argument over bills and stuff.

"My wife and I were having a good night, really—we each had a few drinks. Nothing major, you know it's Saturday night," he said.

"Don't I know it," I replied.

"Anyhow," he continued, "Jamie (that was his wife's name) started talking about bills coming due and Christmas coming up and things like that. So, I was trying to watch TV and relax. She wouldn't stop, though, so I got up and went into the kitchen to get away from her. She decided to follow me in there and kept getting in my face, so I shoved her away. Jamie bumped her head on the wall—not hard or nothing. She was pissed, though, and she decided to call the police. Once the cops get called, someone is going to jail, so here I am."

I felt bad for him—he did really seem like a nice guy, and he really seemed sorry. I thought, *My problems are not that bad.*

Tim continued talking. "I didn't care; I didn't think I was going to get any sleep anyway."

He told me he was very worried and he didn't know what might happen to him. I told him, "It shouldn't be too bad—your wife loves you, right?"

He replied, "Oh, heck yeah!"

"There you go then—just tell the judge just the way you told me, and it shouldn't be that bad."

Tim looked at me and confessed, "But this is the third time."

"Wow," I said. "That sucks."

"Yeah . . ." he said. That was pretty much the end of our conversation. I fell asleep and slept the rest of the night (what little was left anyway).

"Wood! It's time to go—you have been sprung."

The officer in charge of the jail came and got me and led me to the front of the jail. It was about 7:00 a.m. I realized I had only been in the cell for a few hours.

"Your friend Craig is here to pick you up; he already posted your bail. You will, however, have to blow in a breathalyzer to see if you sobered up."

I was fine with this and blew into the machine (only once this time)—the officer held it up to me and showed me all zeroes on the display.

Craig greeted me by the front desk of the police station. He had a copy of the police report, and he was reading it over. Just then, Craig said, "I don't see anything in the road sobriety test that you failed; everything looks good. All it says is you sang your ABCs—"

I interrupted, "That is the only way I know how to do them."

"Yeah, whatever," Craig replied. "The only other thing I see in here it says you have a horizontal gaze, whatever that means."

"Right," I said. "Whatever that means."

Craig drove us back to the hunting camp. It was the opening day, and at least I was out for that. When we arrived at the camp, the sun was coming up, and everyone was out hunting. I thanked Craig for coming to get me, and after that, I crashed out right away.

Around noon the same day, most everyone hunting started to head back into the camp. I remember someone yelling, "Get up, drunk boy! You owe me money."

I was thinking, *Now the worst part—everyone is going to give me shit about getting arrested.* Apparently, Tom and Craig had woken everyone up when they arrived back at the camp around 3:00 a.m. They had taken up a collection to get the $500 to bail me out, and I now I owed various people various sums of money. I assured everyone I would pay him or her back as soon as I could get to a bank.

A lot of people at the camp were giving me a hard time, and I said, "I wasn't drunk!"

I guess that was not the best thing to say. Most of the camp was saying things like "Sure you weren't drunk—that is why they kept you over night in jail." There were a few guys who actually believed me.

That hunting season wasn't the best for me, needless to say. I did, however, go out hunting on that opening night and bagged a doe. I guess my luck wasn't all bad.

The state police had taken my license, but they had given me a paper one to drive with until my court date. I headed home a few days later and returned to work. This was the busiest time for us carpenters—we were working seven days a week and ten to twelve hours a day building the North American Auto Show that would take place in Detroit in about two months. It really sucked, but I had to tell my boss I needed to take a couple of days off work to drive the four hundred miles back to northern Michigan to attend my court date. It was going to be just before Christmas, we were busy, and I had just taken a week off for hunting season.

I let my boss know, and he was really cool about it. I told him the whole story. He felt bad for me and said, "You need a good lawyer."

"I know," I said. "I have a call into a couple of attorneys from the area right now."

About another week went by, and I remembered I had to call the court about the results of my blood test. I did, and I talked to one of the ladies there who told me the good news that I was not drunk. I told her I had known this all along and asked her what would happen now—would they send me my money and license back? She told me they would probably refund my bond money but they may have destroyed my license.

I said, "What? Why did they do that?" I was pissed. I told the lady, "I was going to be nice about this, but now I think I am going to sue."

Right away she said, "Let me have you talk to the prosecutor." She put him right on the phone.

The prosecutor quickly apologized about the whole incident and told me he would fix it. He assured me I would get my bond money back and the charges would be dismissed. He also stated he would write me a letter to take to the secretary of state to get my license reinstated. He did, and that was the end of that experience. I did write a letter to the judge about how I was treated—I am not sure if it did any good.

What a nightmare! At least I didn't have to take time off work. Years later, when I found out I had narcolepsy, it did make sense the officer had seen something in my eyes that wasn't quite right. I am not sure what she meant about a horizontal gaze, but I did get a song out of it. The chorus goes something like this:

> *You got a horizontal gaze and you better change your ways*
> *Cuz you're too drunk to drive too drunk to drive*
> *Your eyes look like their bleeding and you're swerving and*
> *   your weaving and you're too drunk to drive too drunk*
> *   to drive oh yeah*

Any experience you get a song out of can't be all that bad. I never recorded it, but maybe someday. If my mom was alive, I know what she would say about the song. "Jeffrey, drinking and driving isn't something you should make light of!"

I know, Mom, but I wasn't drunk. That is the point.

I did have many road sobriety tests before and after that fateful November evening, but no more arrests. This is another reason I tell people that narcolepsy can make you look seemingly inebriated from time to time. Really crazy when you think about it.

CHAPTER 5

NARCOLEPSY

A t this point, I think it is a good time to fill the reader in on some of what we know about narcolepsy. According to the Narcolepsy Network,[2] narcolepsy is a neurological sleep disorder that can begin at any age and continue throughout life. The Narcolepsy Network generally believes narcolepsy affects about 1 in every 2,000 people. The disorder seems to affect men and women pretty equally. It's also thought to have about the same prevalence in all races, although I have seen information that shows that in Japan, as many as 1 in 500 are affected.

Predisposition to narcolepsy seems to be genetic. Having the genes does not mean you will have the disorder, but in most cases if you don't carry the genes associated with

---

2 Narcolepsy Network, accessed October 26, 2018, https://narcolepsynetwork.org.

narcolepsy, you probably won't have it. In 1998, researchers at Stanford University discovered two brain chemicals called hypocretins one and two (also called orexin a and b)—these neurotransmitters are involved in the regulation of sleep/wake cycles as well as other bodily functions, such as metabolism. Research has shown that the majority of hypocretin-producing cells, located in the hypothalamus, have been destroyed in the brains of those who develop narcolepsy and cataplexy. Scientists believe that narcolepsy with cataplexy (also called type 1 narcolepsy) is most likely caused by the loss of hypocretins and that narcolepsy without cataplexy (also called type 2 narcolepsy) is likely caused by a defect in the transmission or use of one or both hypocretins. The primary symptoms of narcolepsy are as follows:

- Excessive daytime sleepiness
- Cataplexy (This is the second major symptom of narcolepsy. It is a sudden loss of voluntary muscle control—this can be triggered by emotions such as fear, laughter, surprise, or anger. Cataplexy may occur more frequently during times of stress and fatigue.)
- Disrupted nighttime sleep
- Hypnotic hallucinations
- Sleep paralysis
- And for myself and many other patients, automatic behavior—the performance of routine tasks without awareness is fairly prevalent in many patients

The average person will cycle through his or her sleep cycles with non-rapid-eye-movement sleep for about seventy to ninety minutes before their rapid eye movement (or REM sleep cycle) begins. A person with narcolepsy often begins his or her REM cycle within five minutes of falling asleep.

Consult a doctor if you or anyone suspects you may have a sleep disorder. An overnight sleep study is usually the first major test performed. If it is suspected that a patient has narcolepsy, a daytime sleep test called an MSLT is performed. This test is the best-available current resource for the diagnosis of narcolepsy. A genetic blood test can be performed on the patient to see if the person carries one of the genes associated with narcolepsy or cataplexy. Remember, many people carry these genes, so the blood test should be mostly to rule out narcolepsy. If you don't carry one of the genes, you most likely do not have narcolepsy; if you do carry the genes, more tests should be performed. The presence of the genetic marker only suggests a possible predisposition to narcolepsy. To better understand this fact, a person with a genetic predisposition to any disease or disorder has a greater chance of developing it, but that doesn't mean they will. A person with a genetic disease such as cystic fibrosis or Tay-Sachs disease will be born with the disease if they carry the gene or gene combination associated with that disease.

A person with narcolepsy can go many years without being diagnosed. My first symptoms appeared when I was four— I know this from firsthand accounts of my older siblings.

I was not diagnosed until I was thirty-seven. Narcolepsy can appear as many different disorders and diseases, such as attention-deficit disorder and even epilepsy; sleep apnea may also appear as narcolepsy to the undertrained professional. For these reasons and many more, many people with narcolepsy suffer unknowingly for many years. Narcolepsy with cataplexy, sometimes called type-one narcolepsy, is usually much easier to catch than narcolepsy without cataplexy, sometimes referred to as type-two narcolepsy. This is because cataplexy is almost unique to people with narcolepsy.

Sometimes, narcolepsy can be diagnosed instead of another disease or disorder. Studies have shown that many people with shift-workers disorder have been diagnosed with narcolepsy, only later to find out they have shift-workers disorder.

Narcolepsy has been long thought to mostly occur in younger people or adolescents; the exact cause is still unknown. It is theorized that narcolepsy is set off by a sickness, an environmental trigger, or traumatic experience, usually as a child or adolescent. In some patients, another form of narcolepsy has been thought to be caused by trauma to the head, although this type of narcolepsy seems to be rarer and may or may not be associated with a genetic predisposition to narcolepsy. More research is needed. It is important to note that a traumatic experience is not the same as head trauma. A traumatic experience could be many things, such as rape, being robbed at gunpoint, locked in a closet, surviving an accident, or any experience that can be distressing to the brain. In recent years some researchers have pointed to narcolepsy as a possible auto-immune disease. Hopefully, in the not-too-distant future, more evidence will be discovered that may lead to better treatments or maybe even a cure.

CHAPTER 6

TWIDDLING

Flashback to the early 1970s: I was about four years old, and I would engage in a behavior my father would call twiddling. This is hard to explain, but I would do something odd with my hands. Looking back, my brother, who was twelve at the time, recounted that it was like I was playing a Game Boy, but I had nothing in my hands. Of course, this was many years before such an invention. He also said that I would move around in what seemed to be half-circles, walking and playing my invisible Game Boy.

I remember I would walk around with nothing in my hands and sometimes with something in my hands. I could pick up anything, like a toy or a pencil, and my dad would call them twiddle sticks. At times when this would happen, I would be dancing around like I was playing an invisible Game Boy, and my dad would yell, "Jeffrey, stop it!"

I would almost always stop when he yelled my name. With the benefit of time and research, I have come to a possible conclusion what I was doing.

More than likely, I was engaged in automatic behavior, a common symptom of narcolepsy. I know when I would do this, I was always daydreaming. I still do this to this day—in fact, when I was writing this chapter, I took a break and caught myself doing it again. Sometimes, when I would engage in this behavior, I would pretend in my mind I was outside playing baseball or football or whatever. When my dad would yell for me to stop, I believe a chemical would be released in my brain as a response to me hearing my name. I would then snap out of it, like being released from a hypnotic state. This behavior is most likely a form of the narcolepsy symptom *automatic behavior.*

I continued twiddling for the rest of my childhood. I believe my parents became used to this and never really thought too much about it. My actions at this time were not normal and probably one of the first symptoms of narcolepsy that would occur on a daily basis. Like I mentioned, I still do this, even as an adult.

Other accounts from siblings and relatives of my early symptoms of narcolepsy include falling asleep in the middle of a conversation—this occurred as early as age six and seemed to continue throughout my childhood. On more than one occasion, I woke up with clothes on over my pajamas; I always thought it was someone playing a joke on me. I guess not.

I remember when I was very young, my dreams seemed to really scare me. I thought this was normal—I never dreamed any other way. I remember waking up and not wanting to go back to sleep. Then, one day, I decided to tell my dreams I was not afraid of them and that I was going to tell them what to do. I do not know if someone told me to do this or if I thought of it on my own. It seemed to work very well—I could control the outcome of my dreams, and I was able to fall asleep without being scared. I have told people about that ability throughout my life, but most people looked at me like, *Sure, Jeff.*

When doing research for my book, I found that other people have experienced this ability to control their dreams—it is called lucid dreaming. My five-year-old daughter has recently been awakening from many bad dreams. I mentioned to her to tell her dreams that she is in control and that they can't scare her. She did exactly that, and her dreams seem to have become much nicer at least for the time being. Maybe my father told me the same thing when I was a child—I don't know. I can't ask him since he passed away before I was diagnosed with narcolepsy.

When I was first diagnosed, my doctors and nurses asked me about my dreams—they would ask me if they seemed vivid or strange. I told them, "I don't know. My dreams have always seemed the same to me."

I just figured everyone dreamed like that. Now that I think about it, my dreams are intense and vivid, but they have always been this way. Apparently, narcoleptic patients usually have extreme dreams that can be odder than normal and quite vivid. To me, they are just normal—I never dreamed any other way. This could also be a possible symptom of narcolepsy. My older siblings recalled that I would complain of headaches when I was just four years old. I sort of remember that—I still get headaches to this day, but it is something I have gotten used to. Apparently, this can also be a possible sign of narcolepsy. My daughter has recently started to complain about headaches. At first I was thinking that it is no big deal, but her headaches have continued. At present, I am having her screened for narcolepsy as well as other things. I hope she doesn't have narcolepsy, but if she does, I am going to be on top of it from the get-go.

CHAPTER 7

EARLY CATAPLEXY

Cataplexy is one of the biggest problems many narcoleptics have, and it has affected me most of my life (even though I didn't know it). This takes me back to my junior high. I was in gym class one day, and we had open gym. I remember playing dodge ball. In this particular gym, there was a stage at the far end of the gym. I remember having a blast that day, as I always did when playing dodge ball. The class was divided up into two teams. The team I was on had the stage on our side. Early on in the game, I fell and hit my head on the corner of the stage. I had a pretty good gash above my right eye. I recall my classmates asking me what happened, telling me I seemed to have just fallen with no warning.

I replied, "I guess I slipped or something!"

My mother was called, and I remember she and a brother of mine came to get me. I was in the principal's office when they arrived. The bleeding had stopped, and the principal suggested I should go home for the rest of the afternoon and maybe have a doctor look at me. My mother decided I didn't need stitches or any other medical attention and took me home. After we settled down at home for a while, my mother started asking me many questions.

She suggested that maybe my eyes were awfully red and maybe I was smoking marijuana. This was probably the start of my mother (as well as other adults) accusing me of being on something. The accusations would continue throughout my teen years and well into my adulthood.

Around the same time frame, most likely that year, I recall another falling incident. I was in my house, and I remember having a conversation with my father. I don't remember what we were talking about, but I do remember we were laughing at something very funny. I suddenly fell backward, and my father caught me. He started asking if I was okay, and I did not respond right away. My dad said I seemed really limp. He finally got me to my feet and asked again if I was okay. I told him I was fine. I remember other occurrences of falling that were very similar around the same time frame.

CHAPTER 8

CHESS CLUB

I thought my science teacher was out to get me. If you asked my classmates in my junior high, there was a good chance they would tell you my seventh-grade science teacher was a bit of a hard-ass. I really did have a strange feeling he didn't like me.

On more than one occasion, he had insinuated my eyes were very red or that I seemed a little off. Add my teachers' suspicions with the way my mother was grilling me every day with questions like "Where have you been?" and "Whom were you with?" Most sane teenagers would think someone was out to get them. Not very long into my first semester with my new science teacher, I got a stroke of luck. I joined the chess club, and guess who was in charge of it? Right! My science teacher. He was very impressed with my chess ability. I was good—one of the best, if not the best chess player in the group. After joining the chess club, he got to know me a little better, and I would say he treated me much better. I no longer felt like he was accusing me of being high or on something. Unfortunately, the same couldn't be said for my mother. At this time my mother's suspicions and accusations were just settling in for a long marathon that would take me well into my twenties. In my early teens, I would arrive home from bike rides. On many occasions, my mother would pull me aside and look me over like a piece of fruit at a fruit market. She would ask, "Where have you been? Whom were you with? Why are your eyes so red?"

Sometimes she would ask if I was smoking anything, like marijuana. Of course I would assure her I wasn't, but she never believed me. I remember one time she was talking over with my father about her concern in the next room, and I could hear everything. She was telling my father her suspicions about my alleged drug use. I remember my father raising his voice, saying, "He better not be!" My father looked me over but didn't say anything. My mother's accusations continued almost until the day she died. My father, however, never made me feel that way—he apparently didn't think I was doing drugs.

I was raised Roman Catholic and went to church with my family every Sunday. I also went to catechism until I was eighteen. Catechism is the catholic version of Sunday school. I had one teacher there who seemed to take special interest in me, and I thought she was nice. When my mother would pick me up after class, she would have conversations with her. I thought nothing of it at the time, but my mother sent me on a couple of Catholic retreats at my teacher's recommendations. When my mother had picked me up from one of the retreats, she seemed to pay special attention to me—it was really weird, even for my mother. She was looking at me like I had just been through some sort of new enlightenment. She had this gleam in her eyes. I thought, *Is this what this whole retreat thing was—some sort of way to cure me of my alleged drug problems?*

I don't remember any of my siblings ever having to go to such a retreat, so I don't think I was that far off. A year or so after high school, I showed up at church and saw my catechism teacher who had paid me so much attention as her student. She came over to say hello. I thought she was a nice lady. She asked me how I was doing, and I told her I was doing well. She then said, "That is good. I know you were quite messed up on drugs in high school!"

I was shocked, I thought, *What a witch,* and just walked away. I never went near that lady again. In fact, I really never liked going to that church again. During high school, I did well in most subjects—in fact I was totally acing English, and I really enjoyed the class and my teacher. However my grades in my last semester of my senior year really fell in that class. I remember a discussion with my English teacher after school one day before I graduated. She said to me, "Jeff, I don't understand what happened, your work has really started to fall off, and you were doing so well in my class. Then, in the last couple of months, your work has really gone south."

I told her I don't know why, but I am sure it wasn't her fault; she was one of my favorite teachers. I don't know for sure, but my sudden drop in grades could have something to do with my undiagnosed narcolepsy at the time, or it could just have been me being a teenager. More than likely, it was a little of both.

CHAPTER 9
MORE CATAPLEXY

My cataplexy has become worse as I have gotten older. I was diagnosed with narcolepsy and cataplexy at age thirty-seven. Amazingly, I had many severe cataplexy occurrences throughout my life, and nobody caught it.

One incident happened when I was around the age of thirty. I recall installing drywall in a house with a few coworkers of mine. As lunchtime approached, Ken, the boss on the job, asked what everyone wanted for lunch. We all agreed on pizza. Ken told us all to ante up. We all gave him money, and he headed out to get our lunch. When Ken came back, he yelled, "Come on, you board dogs. It's lunchtime!

We sat down and enjoyed our lunch. As usual, many stories and jokes were told. After a time, Ken yelled, "Let's get this house done!"

We all stood up, but one more joke had to be told. I don't remember the joke, but I do remember laughing intensely. Just then, I fell backward to the ground. Everyone stopped, and Ken yelled, "Are you okay?"

After a few moments, I responded "Yes, I am okay."

Ken said, "What the heck happened?"

I replied, "I don't know. I guess I slipped."

We went on about our day, and nothing was ever mentioned again about the incident.

Around the same time in my life, a more embarrassing situation happened while I was at a John Cougar Mellencamp concert. My friends and I had pretty good seats, but it is always fun to get as close as you can. Slowly but surely, as the crowd became more exited and everyone started to stand, we began our journey to the front of the stage. We ended up front row center stage, and we rocked to a few anthems and sang our throats dry.

Suddenly a bouncer appeared and asked to see our tickets. Immediately he realized that these were not our seats, and he began to escort us back to our row. While walking up the aisle back to our seats, I collapsed to the ground. Everyone stopped, and the bouncer cleared a space for me and began asking me if I was okay. I lay there motionless for what seemed like a long time while people discussed what to do.

The bouncer must have thought I was drunk. I wasn't, but I was totally shocked. I slowly rose to my feet. An ambulance was called; the paramedics put me on a gurney and checked my vitals. They suggested I go to the hospital, but I refused, claiming I felt good and I was okay. By this time, the concert was over, and I felt like I already ruined everyone's night.

CHAPTER 10

FIELD TRIP

L ike I mentioned before, I have had a lot of trouble with driving and tickets in my life. One time when I was in my early twenties, I was fighting a ticket in court. That day, there was also an elementary school at court on a field trip. I was only fighting a speeding ticket of five to ten over— at the time, I had several points on my driving record for small infractions such as the one I was fighting. Obviously, my car insurance was quite expensive, and the fear of losing my license for too many points was always haunting me.

As I mentioned, an elementary school was in the court room on a field trip. The judge talked to the children throughout the court proceedings and described to the children what was relevant for each defendant. The judge noted that everyone's driving record would be different. The more moving violations on a defendants record, the longer the sheet of paper would be that the judge would be looking at. The judge would show the paper length to the students every time a new defendant would appear before the judge. Most were short, just a few inches in length. When the judge came to one that was much larger, the students gasped, almost in fear. The judge said that record wasn't that bad and that he would let them know when he had a really long one. Then it happened; the judge came to my case and my record. He called "Jeffrey Wood to the stand!" I stood up and was sworn in. The judge pulled out my record, and my piece of paper was many inches long—by far the longest one of the day. The children gasped in horror and looked at me like I was an evil ogre. The judge told the children that this was a very bad record. At that time, all I wanted to do was disappear. I never thought I would win my case, but I knew I should at least fight it—any more tickets and I could lose my license or have to pay so much for car insurance I wouldn't be able to afford to drive.

The judge reamed me good—he told me to pay the ticket and never come back to his court. I said, "Yes, sir!"

When I left the courtroom, the children were staring at me in disbelief. I think they expected someone would come and arrest me and throw away the key. I couldn't wait to get out of there and hoped no one there knew me—what a nightmare. Who would have thought an elementary school would take a field trip to court, and on the day I was fighting a traffic ticket? It was like I was in a movie or something.

CHAPTER 11

MISPLACED

I love the outdoors, and I spend a lot of time hunting and fishing. My father's family is from northern Michigan, so I spend a lot of time up there. One hunting season, a friend and I were hunting deep in the woods in an area we call the Oaks. I have hunted around the same oak tree for years—a beautiful tree nestled in among many other oaks; hence why the area is called the Oaks. After an unsuccessful morning hunt, my friend and I decided to get lunch. We changed into our street clothes and headed to a local tavern. When we arrived, I couldn't find my wallet. My friend Mark asked, "Where did you have it last?"

I said, "If I knew that, I would know where it is."

We headed back to the cabin, and I tore everything apart, but no luck I couldn't find it. Mark suggested we go back to the woods near my tree stand and look for it. When we got there, Mark asked me what color it was. I told him it was camouflage. He said, "Really, what the heck are you doing with a camouflage wallet!"

I told him my dad had given it to me for a Christmas gift. He replied, "Your dad should know better than that—if anything, he should have given you a hunter's orange one."

We laughed, but it wasn't funny. We searched everywhere in the woods for a camouflage wallet, and of course we found nothing. Later, as we were getting ready for the evening hunt, there was my wallet—it was in my hunting boot. What luck!

Everybody loses things from time to time, but for me, it is constant. Another time at a hunting camp, one of the older gentlemen shot a doe. It was around noon, and I ran into him at the hunting camp. He asked if I would help him retrieve the deer and field dress it. I agreed, and we headed to his blind and found the deer lying about one hundred feet away. I dragged the deer out of the way and proceeded to gut it. We cleaned up, I dragged the deer back to his truck, and we loaded it. We returned to the camp and hung the deer on the buck pole.

I realized I didn't have my cell phone. I asked Dave, the man I helped with the deer, if he could call my phone for me, and he did. I looked and listened everywhere I thought it might be, but I couldn't hear it anywhere. I hoped I didn't have the ringer silenced. I kept looking; I couldn't find it. Dave suggested we go back in the woods and look for it, so we did. We were looking all over by his deer blind and where we dragged the deer, but we found nothing. Dave suggested we call my phone.

I said, "We can try, but a lot of times, you can't receive a cell-phone signal that far back in the woods."

He tried, and sure enough, we heard it ringing. We listened and looked everywhere on the ground but couldn't find it. I asked Dave to try again—we were close. It rang again, and I knew I was right on top of it. Then I heard it really well.

"Oh no," I shouted. "It is under the gut pile!"

I felt around in the bloody mess, and there it was all covered in blood—it was amazing it still worked. We headed back to the camp, and Dave told everyone the story. They all laughed, and so did I. This was well before I was diagnosed with narcolepsy.

One Sunday morning, I woke up and headed by myself to breakfast. It was fall and football season, and I like to read about my team, the Lions, in the Sunday sports section. I parked my car at the restaurant I was going to, and just then, I remembered I needed a newspaper. I walked into the gas station next door to the restaurant and purchased one. When I walked out of the door of the gas station, I looked for my car by the gas pump. I didn't see it. I ran to the other side of the gas station—and no car. I hurried and dialed 911 to report my car stolen. I was describing the car to the 911 operator when I looked over to the restaurant parking lot next door, and there it was—my car. I was totally embarrassed, and I told the 911 operator I was sorry, but my car wasn't stolen—I had just forgotten where I parked it. This type of thing is more the norm for me than someone might think.

I have probably lost my wallet more than a hundred times—maybe even closer to two hundred times. Almost all the time I eventually found it, with a few exceptions. I have learned to never carry money in my wallet and as little identification as I can get away with.

While writing this book, I shared with a friend of mine that I bet I spend more than an hour a day looking for stuff. He said, "I bet it is more than that."

What most people don't understand when I explain my problem with losing things, is that I put things where they are supposed to go. For example, I hang my keys up by the door; my wallet and phone go on my bed stand at night. I have a place for everything that is important. When I am losing or misplacing things, I am doing what is known in the narcolepsy world as automatic behavior. It is hard to understand, but throughout the day, I am visibly awake, but not 100 percent—I am awake, but I am unaware. I do things that I have done many of times, almost perfect, but if there is something a little different, it can cross me up. This is why I lose so many things; I am not totally awake all the time, so I leave things where I don't remember leaving them.

Unfortunately I can lose just about anything at any time, and this problem can get really expensive. I have left anything from luggage to diaper bags and even musical instruments in crazy places. Once, I lost a brand-new cordless drill in a case; it was worth about $200. I left it on the side of the road where you may put your garbage cans. That day, my truck was parked on the street, and I was loading up my vehicle after finishing remodeling a basement. When I arrived home that night, I noticed it was missing. I went back the next day, but I couldn't find it. I didn't get the cordless drill back. Most of the time, I realize I lost something sooner rather than later, and I usually get it back. One Saturday evening, my band was playing at a bar downtown. I left my bass guitar in an alley, and I discovered it was gone when I got home that night. I headed back to the bar, and there it was in the alley, right by where I loaded up my band equipment. Thank God—I got lucky that time. Shortly after I was diagnosed with narcolepsy, my older brother had to be rushed to the hospital; I met him there and learned he would be spending the night. He handed over some of his personal belongings to me. His checkbook was among these possessions. I managed to keep track of most of his stuff—I did, however, misplace his checkbook. The day he was to be discharged from the hospital, I drove to pick him up. The first thing he said to me was "Hey, give me my checkbook." I knew I had lost it, so I told him I wasn't sure where it was right then.

He responded, "What?"

I said, "I am sure I will find it. I have all the rest of your stuff." I thought he was going to freak out on me, but instead, he busted out laughing. I turned to him and asked what was so funny.

He said, "I should have known better than to give the narcoleptic something so important."

I said, "Yeah, funny." I was glad he was not mad.

I did find his checkbook about six months later, and I mailed it to him. He called me and told me I didn't have to do that, as he had already canceled that whole book of checks.

Having narcolepsy and losing things is not all bad. Some days it can be like winning the lotto. Every now and then, I will find twenty or sometimes even one hundred dollars or more—money I forgot I lost or had given up on. You wouldn't believe how many times I lost my wallet and had to get a new driver's license only to find it a week or two later.

It is true that everybody loses things, but when you have narcolepsy, it can be an everyday experience. I really need you to understand that this is not like the normal person losing things on occasions; everybody does that. I try very hard to stay as organized as possible. I only pay bills and do other important things when I know I am most alert. Just recently, I was cleaning up my boat motor for the upcoming fishing season—I had work clothes on, and I ended up with gas all over my pants, which is okay because I had work pants on. When I finished with my motor, I went inside to clean up, take a shower, and put new clothes on to go out to dinner. It was Saturday night, and I had a good time at dinner and then played darts at a tavern with a couple of friends. I was home by midnight, but that is late for me, and I crashed out right away. I woke up the next morning, took a shower, and proceeded to get dressed for the day. I opened up my pants drawer, and I was hit with a huge whiff of gasoline. Apparently, when I had changed the night before, I put my dirty clothes back in my dresser—the ones that had the gas all over them. I decided after that to wash all my clothes in that dresser just to make sure I got the smell of gas out. Almost all narcoleptics I have talked to have had similar experiences, like putting milk in the kitchen cabinet or laundry in the refrigerator. I tell my family and friends that this may be what I hate worst about narcolepsy.

CHAPTER 12

SEEMINGLY INEBRIATED

S plash! "Is everything okay? Let me get something to wipe this up."

The waitress rushed to get some rags, because I had just dropped my coffee all over the table at a restaurant I frequented. Cindy, the waitress, said she was coming to check on me, and she saw me just staring off blankly when I dropped my cup. I have been to this restaurant on many occasions, and I remember thinking she probably thought I was drunk.

I definitely dropped things from time to time throughout my adulthood. This was occurring more often; just the day before at work, I had dropped my metal framing clamps from the scaffold to the ground a half a dozen times in just a few minutes. Sal, my partner, said, "It is a good thing this is a hard-hat job. Have you been drinking?"

Of course, Sal knew I hadn't been drinking. We drove to work together, and he had been with me all day. He decided it would be best if he worked on top of the scaffold the rest of the day. "Maybe I can try to knock you out for a change," he said jokingly.

Dropping tools and cups only became more prevalent as I grew older. Also, staring off at nothing became more noticeable by other people. At this point in my life, accusations like being drunk or high on something became more commonplace. Looking back, I can't really blame people. I know I must have appeared seemingly inebriated to many people, especially the ones who didn't know me very well.

I can't say for sure how many road sobriety tests I have been subjected to, but I know it was at least a dozen. I passed them all. For whatever reason, my narcolepsy makes me appear drunkish at times throughout the day. Slurring my words in the middle of a conversation is not uncommon for me. This, like many of my symptoms, has become more prevalent as I age; in fact my speech issues are now an everyday appearance, although I seem to catch myself most of the time and I am able to keep it under the radar, so to speak. I usually just stop talking and take a break, depending on the situation.

Dropping things is a form of cataplexy, as well as slurring words. Another thing that can make me appear drunk is the fact sometimes I will stumble when walking. At our hunting camp, I earned the nickname "Stumble and Shoot." Whenever one of my brothers would hear me shoot during hunting season, they would comment, "Do you think Jeff shot a deer, or do you think he fell down?"

Hence the name Stumble and Shoot. For the record, I never really fell in the woods when carrying a gun—my bros just liked messing with me. This is also caused by cataplexy.

CHAPTER 13

DATING WITH NARCOLEPSY

D ating with narcolepsy and relationships can be quite difficult, especially when you do not know you have narcolepsy yet. This brings me back to the summer of 1989. I had met a young lady at a church fair. She seemed nice, and we hung out at the fair for a couple of hours, and we exchanged phone numbers. As dating goes, we talked on the phone a couple of times and decided to make a date.

She lived about forty minutes from where I lived, and we were both about twenty-one. I picked her up around five o'clock on a Saturday evening. To start the date, we went to dinner. This was your average dinner date—a little talking, a little eating, and just getting to know each other.

After dinner we went to a small sports bar where we had a few drinks and played darts. Everything was going fine.

We seemed to be getting along well. It wasn't late yet. It was only around 10:00 p.m., so the night was still young.

At the time, we were both living with our parents. We talked about what to do next and decided to get a hotel room—maybe not to spend the whole night but to have a place to go and watch TV or something.

Of course this was my first real date with her, and I didn't think anything would happen much physically. We arrived at the hotel around ten thirty, and we had picked up some munchies and soda pop. We sat on the bed and started to watch a movie.

I remember kissing a little bit, but unfortunately that is all I remember, until about 1:00 a.m. This is when I woke up on the bed, and my date was looking at me kind of bewildered. I said to her, "Boy, I must have fallen asleep!"

She replied, "Yes, you did."

She decided it was time for me to take her home. To this day, I do not know when I fell asleep, but I guess it was right away. It pissed me off that I fell asleep—no matter what was going to happen, I was having a good time with this lady on my date.

I continued to take her home and dropped her off at her dad's house, walked her to the door, and kissed her goodnight. I waited until Monday and decided to call her, even though I was very embarrassed about what had happened. I talked to her for a few minutes, and of course I asked her for another date. She said no, and like an idiot I had to ask her why.

Of course she said, "Do you have to ask why?"

I said no, and that was the end of it. It really sucked, because I really liked her. She was easygoing, we had good conversation, and she was attractive. Similar occurrences plagued my dating life throughout my twenties and thirties.

I remember a lady I knew in my twenties. We were friends, and we attended many of the same social functions. I was attracted to her and asked her out a few times. No was always the answer, so eventually, I stopped asking. We remained friends and ran into each other at social events throughout the next few years. Finally, I found out she was going to be married. And the next time I saw her, I congratulated her, and we talked for a while. I mentioned how it was interesting that we got along well but never went on a date. She replied to me that one of the reasons she never went out with me was she thought I partied too much and that I seemed high all the time. I said, "Really, that's what you thought?"

She said it really seemed that way. I am sure I may have had a couple of beers sometimes when I saw her, but I definitely didn't smoke pot or use any illegal drugs. It was surprising how many people in my life thought I was high all the time.

In 2005, when I was finally diagnosed with narcolepsy and cataplexy, I started taking medications for my symptoms. One such medication was Xyrem. This medication was unique because I had to take it in two doses. I would take one dose just before I fell asleep. I then would have to set an alarm for four hours later to wake up and take another dose. A year or so later, I met a woman. I liked her, and I decided to let her move in with me. I had discussed my medical conditions with her, and she said she was okay with it. Things seemed okay at first—my narcolepsy didn't seem to cause much of an issue with our relationship. It didn't take long, however, and my girlfriend started complaining about my medicine. She really had a hard time understanding why I would have to wake up to take medicine just to go right back to sleep again. Eventually we had to sleep in different rooms, and our relationship didn't last much longer. She eventually moved out, and I was single again.

Dating was always challenging for me, before and after I was finally diagnosed with narcolepsy. At this time in my life, I am recently divorced—I had a three-year marriage. My wife knew about my narcolepsy—I had told her right away when we first started dating. Through the divorce proceedings, my narcolepsy played a large role in much of my court case. I am currently starting to date again. I am not sure when I should bring up my issues with my narcolepsy and cataplexy. It mostly depends on the situation and the other person. I do not want to waste anybody's time, and I don't want the person to think I'm being dishonest. One of the hardest things is to explain to someone what narcolepsy is and what it isn't. In my opinion, all the information and misinformation on the Internet doesn't make it any easier. This is one reason I am writing this book—to give other people the best insight I can to help them understand what narcolepsy is and what issues people like myself have to deal with.

CHAPTER 14

NAP TIME

At this time, if you have narcolepsy, you may want to take a nap.

zzzzzzzzzzzzzzzzzzzzzzzzzzzzzzzzzzzzzzzzzzzzzzzzzzzzzzzzzzzzzzzz
zzzzzzzzzzzzzzzzzzzzzzzzzzzzzzzzzzzzzzzzzzz

zzzzzzzzzzzzzzzzzzzzzzzzzzzzzzzzzzzzzzzzzzzzzzzzzzzzzzzzzzzzzzzz
zzzzzzzzzzzzzzzzzzzzzzzzzzzzzzzzzzzzzzzzzzz

CHAPTER 15

RAT RACE

"What are we doing tonight?" Matt asked.

Paul said, "Dinner's ready; let's eat."

The three of us sat down at the table in Brother Paul's cabin on the family property in the upper peninsula of Michigan that I frequently vacation to. Paul had just installed Dish Network—a major deal for our rustic property. Someone asked what we should watch, and Paul responded, "Have you guys seen this movie called *Rat Race*[3]? Whoopee Goldberg and Newman from Seinfeld are in it, and a bunch of other famous actors. It's hilarious."

We proceeded to watch the movie. The first scene was set in Vegas. The plot was based on a room full of millionaires

---

3 *Rat Race*, directed by Jerry Zucker, United States: Fireworks Pictures, 2001.

who would bet on anything just for the fun of it. The ultra-rich guys were bored with their little side bets. When they spied an unlikely and unique bunch of vacationers to the sin city, they watched them on a bunch of hidden cameras located around the casino. Every rich guy picked a tourist or two to bet on. The object was to get the participants they selected to go on a race to California. The winner of the race would receive a million dollars. One of the millionaires picked Enrico Pollini, played by Rowan Atkinson. Enrico had a very rare disorder called narcolepsy. He would be walking, and all of a sudden, he would stop and close his eyes and appear to fall in a very deep sleep while standing. The millionaires thought that was hilarious. This occurred once when he was crossing the street, near the casino. All of a sudden, cars were slamming on their brakes. There was Enrico, just standing there sleeping while standing, sound asleep like a baby, horns honking, people yelling, but nothing disturbing him. Then, abruptly, he would snap out of it and finish crossing the street like nothing happened.

"Ha-ha, Jeff, that's you—the guy on the TV with the rare disorder," my brothers exclaimed hysterically. I had never heard of this, and neither had my brothers. We thought it was just made up for the movie.

This was toward the fall of 2004—I remember this because my father had just passed away in June of that year. At this time in my life, my symptoms were becoming more and more noticeable. My father suffered from COPD as well as other ailments like heart disease. He had several doctors, including an ear, nose, and throat doctor. Apparently, my father had discussed my sleeping issues with his doctor and urged me to make an appointment. My father mentioned the doctor thinks I may have sleep apnea. Later the same summer, my dad passed away. Later that same year, I remember one of my brothers and I gave an electrician a ride home from work because his car had broken down. My family was all carpenters, and we would work a lot on the same job sites, so we would drive to work together often. The electrician shared with us that he just began using oxygen while sleeping at night. Apparently he was diagnosed with sleep apnea. He mentioned that he would get really tired while driving. After using what he called a CPAP machine at night while sleeping for a few weeks, he wasn't sleepy at all. It seemed like he solved his sleeping problem. My brother heard his story and said, "That sounds like you, Jeff!"

I responded, "Maybe."

I thought it would be cool if I could figure out what was making me so tired all the time. It was about six months later when I finally had a doctor get me in for a sleep study. I spent a whole night at a sleep clinic attached to the hospital. I was hooked up to a bunch of wires, and they told me to sleep, so I did. The results? No sleep apnea. More tests were needed. I never ever had a problem sleeping, but staying awake—that was always an issue. My doctor reviewed my sleep study and discussed my symptoms, including what he called cataplexy. Then, he diagnosed me with narcolepsy. I had never heard of narcolepsy—wait a minute! I had heard of it in that movie *Rat Race*. Ha-ha, brothers. You're right; that is me.

The following is a graph from my overnight sleep study:

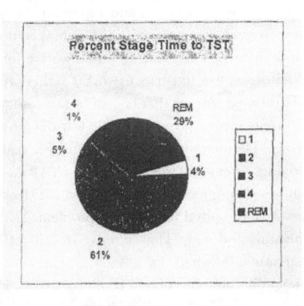

CHAPTER 16

FINALLY

Finally, I had some answers. I know what you're thinking—why did it take so long for me to get diagnosed with narcolepsy? First, I would have to know I had something definitely wrong with me. I never really noticed my early symptoms, like dosing off as a kid when carrying on conversations with friends and relatives. Other symptoms, like my automatic behavior, I'm sure, just seemed normal after a while to my parents. I grew up with five siblings. There was always a lot going on in my house, and my parents probably thought my behavior was normal—at least for me. Maybe they thought I would grow out of it. In hindsight, my early cataplexy should have been a red flag, but no one even thought much about it. My mom was sure I was on drugs or something from the time I was a teenager up until before she passed away in 1993. When my mom was sick in the hospital shortly before she died, we had conversations about my health situation. I was twenty-five at the time. By then, she was satisfied that I wasn't on any drugs. However, she made me promise to see a doctor when I could. Later that year, sometime after my mom's funeral, I did. At twenty-five, I hadn't been to a doctor's office very often, so I had to seek one out.

Pretty much the only symptom I could describe at the time was being very tired while driving. I remember going to this one doctor for the first time. He did a physical and took some blood tests, and I made an appointment to come back and review the results. He came into the room where the nurse had left me and looked over my chart. He said to me, "You get really tired when driving, right?"

"Yeah," I said. He said that he used to have the same problem.

I said, "Really?

"He said, "Yes, until I stopped drinking."

I was shocked—I didn't know what to say to the dick-head. That was the end of me seeking out help from doctors, at least for a little while. A few more years passed by, and my sleepiness kept getting gradually worse. In addition, a lot of other crazy things kept happening. I decided to give the doctor thing another try. I found a different doctor, and this one didn't even invite me back for a second look. I told him about the things that were going on with my exhaustion and other issues. He decided I should see a psychiatrist, and he gave me a card for one. I never called the psychiatrist, and I thought this doctor was just another jackass like all the rest.

I didn't give up. A few more years went by, and I found another doctor who seemed pretty good. This doctor really listened to me and did many tests. I figured, *Why not?* I had great insurance through my carpenters union, and I never really used it. He conducted a bunch of different blood tests until he finally started to lean toward the possibility that I was diabetic. When he tested my sugar, it was elevated—I thought I did have a sweet tooth. He conducted a glucose-tolerance test next, which was no fun—I had to drink sugary liquids and wait in the office as he checked my sugar after a little while. I seemed to pass the tolerance test quite well, although the doctor noted I may be prediabetic.

About this time, I was thirty-four, and my father was in and out of the hospital with various problems with his heart and lungs. I remember spending a lot of time with him then, and we often discussed my health issues. I was always in great physical shape. The issues I dealt with were internal: my sleepiness issues and my high cholesterol. The only time I had ever been hospitalized was in 1995 when I had my appendix removed, and that went quite well.

My new doctor seemed to be doing a good job, checking out the various possibilities of what might be wrong with me. This was a really stressful time for me with my father being sick. I do not remember why I stopped going to this doctor, but I do remember that he retired from his practice about the same time my father was getting really sick and I never really got a chance to follow up with him. By the time my father passed away, I knew my problem had something to do with sleep, just like my dad said. By this time it was 2005, and sleep was a big business. I finally got in touch with some good doctors, and we were on our way to figuring things out. My neurologist at this time started me on Adderall; I took a dose in the morning and also another one in the afternoon if I needed it. The results were awesome—I had never felt so good in my life. I remember calling my sister up and telling her I felt like I was awake for the first time.

At the next appointment with my neurologist, I told him the good news. Dr. K was happy for me, but he did caution me. He mentioned that in time, the medicine wouldn't work as well for me and I would need to increase my dosage or try other medicines. Eventually, he explained I would be on a drug cocktail. I heeded his warnings, but for now, I was happy. Who would have thought? All my life people thought I was on drugs, and I wasn't. Now, I was on medicine, and I felt totally normal.

CHAPTER 17

YOU'RE A SICK MAN!

"You're sick. You're a sick man!" exclaimed the judge. I stood there in shock—I really didn't know what to think. After all, I was only in court to fight a simple traffic ticket for running a red light. This was the summer of 2005, shortly after I was diagnosed with narcolepsy. At this time, I had just begun addressing my symptoms. I discussed the incident with my neurologist before going to court, and he wrote me a note to take to court. All my adult life, I had a bad driving record. Most of my tickets were for things like going five to ten miles over the speed limit in areas where the speed limit suddenly would change. Other tickets included infractions for no turn on red where I may have not noticed the sign indicating not to.

I finally realized (with the help of my neurologist) that this was due in part because of my narcolepsy and the fact

I did not yet know I had the disease. What happens some-times when I am driving is I don't fall asleep but I become slightly dazed—almost hypnotized. My eyes don't close. I am still functioning, but I am not 100 percent alert.

My diagnosis came a few weeks before I had my court date to fight my traffic ticket. My medicine seemed to be working really well, and I was excited to say the least. I had finally found out what was causing the weird experiences that plagued me most of my life especially while driving. I was in court to fight my traffic ticket, yes, but I was also there to explain that I now know the reason for my not-so-perfect driving. I also wanted to explain what I was doing about it. I did not expect the judge to dismiss the ticket—I really just wanted to say I was sorry and that it won't happen again.

The morning of my court date, I showed up on time and signed in with the clerk. I then took a seat in the court room with all the other defendants. After waiting awhile, my name was finally called, and I stood up to be sworn in by the judge. I asked the judge if I could approach the bench and hand him my doctor's note. The judge allowed me to approach, and I handed him my note. He looked at the note, and to my surprise, he became quite frantic.

The judge said, "So, so what? You're sick. You're a sick man! You should not have been driving!"

The other people in the court room looked at me like I was crazy. At that moment, I felt like I was. I was not allowed to say anything. He told me to pay the ticket, so I left the room and did just that.

I proceeded to the parking lot where I sat in my vehicle in shock after what had just happened. It was one of the worst feelings of my life—I was thinking about what the judge said, and I felt like an outcast. At this time, I was still just learning about narcolepsy, and I knew very little about it.

While sitting in the parking lot, I remembered that I had a brochure from the Narcolepsy Network. I decided to call the number on the pamphlet. A warm, friendly voice answered the phone, and I told the lady why I was calling and what just happened to me. I could tell that she felt bad for me, but after talking to her, I felt a lot better. She assured me that I wasn't a sick man—at least not in the way the judge made it sound. It was like talking to a shrink.

This was the beginning of my research and understanding of narcolepsy, cataplexy, and other problems that may come with this unique medical condition. For the record, I have never had another ticket while driving. Now that I have a better understanding of my condition, I never drive if I am even remotely tired, and I take the proper medication to reduce the risk of issues arising.

After my discussion with the Narcolepsy Network, I decided to learn more about this condition that I had. I read up on it and realized that I had never even had an MSLT test, which is the most reliable test for narcolepsy. I found another neurologist, and we performed the MSLT test. Before the test my new doctor cautioned me that no matter what the test results are, we were going to treat my symptoms that suggest narcolepsy. I agreed.

The MSLT test is a sleep study that is done during the day. During the test, the patient is led into a room with a bed and a TV, much like a small hotel room. Then, the patient is hooked up to many wires around their head and other parts of the body. Once hooked up to all the diagnostic equipment, the patient is asked to sleep for about fifteen minutes; after that time, the sleep technician will wake the patient up and keep the patient awake for about forty-five minutes. After this time goes by, the patient has to sleep for another fifteen minutes. This cycle is repeated four to five times, depending on the patient. The object of the test is to see whether the patient can fall asleep in such a short time frame and, if they do, whether the patient cycles into REM sleep. A normal person won't fall into a REM cycle for about seventy minutes. A person with narcolepsy, however, will often fall into REM sleep within minutes—sometimes even seconds. If the patient falls into REM quickly in at least one or more of the sleep sessions, a diagnosis of narcolepsy is probable. When the test results came back, they were positive for narcolepsy. I had fallen into REM sleep almost right away.

After that, I asked to get the genetic test just to know which genes I carry, and the results were positive. I carried two genes associated with narcolepsy. The genes I carry are HLA DRB1*15 Positive, and HLA DQB1*0602 Positive. Other gene combinations associated with narcolepsy are as follows: HLA DRB1*15 negative/HLA DQB1*0602 Positive;

HLA DRB1*15 Positive/HLA DQB1*0602 Negative. My first neurologist was right in his diagnosis of narcolepsy, and I am grateful to him; however I am glad I have had the more current and up-to-date test for narcolepsy. After all these years going undiagnosed, I wanted to be totally sure what I was dealing with.

The following is a page from my MSLT:

Nap 1   Nap Start: 8:03:51 AM   Nap End: 8:22:21 AM

Latency to Sleep Onset: 5.0m
Total Sleep Time: 15.5m

Times	REM	Stg. 1	Stg. 2	Stg. 3	Stg. 4
	12.0m	2.5m	1.0m	0.0m	0.0m

Nap 2   Nap Start: 10:08:26 AM   Nap End: 10:31:52 AM

Latency to Sleep Onset: 8.0m
Total Sleep Time: 14.5m

Times	REM	Stg. 1	Stg. 2	Stg. 3	Stg. 4
	1.0m	8.5m	5.0m	0.0m	0.0m

Nap 3   Nap Start: 12:01:36 PM   Nap End: 12:18:35 PM

Latency to Sleep Onset: 2.0m
Total Sleep Time: 15.5m

Times	REM	Stg. 1	Stg. 2	Stg. 3	Stg. 4
	0.0m	3.5m	12.0m	0.0m	0.0m

Nap 4   Nap Start: 2:02:03 PM   Nap End: 2:21:46 PM

Latency to Sleep Onset: 6.0m
Total Sleep Time: 13.5m

Times	REM	Stg. 1	Stg. 2	Stg. 3	Stg. 4
	0.0m	8.5m	5.0m	0.0m	0.0m

MEAN SLEEP LATENCY IN (4) NAPS: 5.5 MINUTES, 2 SOREMPS.

INTERPRETATION: MODERATE EDS, 2 SOREMPS.

CHAPTER 18

WORKING WITH NARCOLEPSY

Working with narcolepsy can be a bit of a challenge, and for me, it was more than that. The fact that I wasn't diagnosed with narcolepsy until I was thirty-seven years old meant I was dealing with an undiagnosed and untreated condition for a very long time.

I have had narcolepsy for most of (if not all) my life. I would have to say knowing you have something wrong with you makes it easier to deal with than if you don't. The fact that many people thought I was high or otherwise inebriated most of the time didn't help things out much.

After high school, I joined the Carpenters Union and began serving a four-year apprenticeship. Carpentry seemed to be a good fit for me. I was always a hustler and hard worker. Looking back, it would have been almost impossible for me to fall asleep at work—I was always running. If I had a job where I sat behind a desk all day, this may have been a different story.

As an apprentice, many coworkers (as well as some of my foremen) would mention my appearance of possibly being high. Some carpenters I worked with would smoke weed or drink beer. In a weird way, I fit in well with them—remember, I didn't know something was wrong with me at the time. Most companies I worked for would not send me to a job site with mandatory drug testing, assuming I couldn't pass one. That was fine with me—most of the drug-testing jobs were in downtown Detroit at the time, and parking was a nightmare. Most of the other work sites without drug testing were easier to access.

I actually didn't smoke weed, and I only drank beer on weekends and other occasions. It was definitely not something I partook in every day. Most people were shocked when they found out I didn't smoke weed, and I think very few believed it. Looking back, I can understand why they thought that. My condition did make me seem a little off at times.

As a construction worker, I would sometimes have to drive many miles to work. By the time I was in my midthirties, this became quit a burden on me. It got to the point where I would get a hotel room at least one night a week, even though the drive home was less than one hour. I recall one job that lasted about six months. The job was only a thirty-minute drive, at night though; with traffic it could be a lot longer. For this particular job, I would pick up an apprentice carpenter every morning who was in need of a ride to work. His name was Jonathon, and he was good company for me. Having someone with me made the drive to and from work pass by easily.

A few months into this job, Jonathon asked if I was okay. I asked him what he meant, and he told me that he had noticed something on our rides home. I was surprised and asked him what he meant. He said that sometimes I seemed like a zombie. He told me that my driving was all right (I made all the correct stops and everything), but I seemed like I was on autopilot.

Jonathon and I would take the same route into and home from work each day. I asked Jonathon, "Did I almost get in an accident or something?"

"No," Jonathon replied. "Nothing like that. You just seem like you're not completely here—especially on the drives home."

"Okay, Jonathon," I replied. "Let me know if you think I should pull over or something."

"Okay," he said.

I would later find out that I had been driving like this for most of my life. This type of behavior is considered automatic behavior, one of the most telling signs of narcolepsy. A lot of people with narcolepsy will drive like this before they are diagnosed. Usually, if a narcoleptic travels the same way each day, they become used to the route and can follow it even though they are not totally alert. This is a problem that can easily be fixed with a proper diagnosis and medicine.

When describing narcolepsy to people, I have noticed many of them assume that narcoleptics fall asleep when driving. Most people are not aware that many times, this is not the case. Many narcoleptics drive in this automatic behavior–type trance where their eyes are open, but they are not fully alert. This is another reason narcolepsy goes unnoticed in many patients.

Many years later, I ran into Jonathon. I told him how I was diagnosed with narcolepsy and proceeded to explain the way the disease works to him. Jonathon told me, "Wow, that all makes sense now."

By the time I was finally diagnosed with narcolepsy, I was thirty-seven. At this time, I started taking medicine, and it seemed to help a great deal. I had to mention the fact that I had narcolepsy to my boss at the time. This was 2005, and almost every job I worked on now had mandatory drug testing. I wanted to let them know in case anything might happen. I was quite worried about what might happen when I brought this up to my boss, Ronald. One morning, before work, I told him that I had narcolepsy. Ronald replied, "Okay, so?"

I told him I wanted to let him know because I was on medication for it, and even though the medicine was working well, I wanted him to know in case something happened. Ronald replied, "You are not going to fall asleep on me, are you?"

I told him this was very unlikely because I was responding well to the medication. That answer satisfied him, and he even joked to me about whether the medicine I was on was like speed. I told him it was something like that, and he joked that maybe we could get some for the other guys. We both laughed, and that was the end of it. And I went to work feeling pretty good.

Working as a carpenter with narcolepsy had been going pretty well for a couple of years. But as time went on, I had to increase my medicines, and my narcolepsy kept getting worse. Just waking up in the morning became a major issue. All my life I had considered myself a morning person. I loved getting up early and working at sunup, especially when I was working outside. Now, just getting to work on time was becoming a major problem. One job site I worked on had a rule that if you were late for work, you had to buy donuts for the crew. This became quite expensive for me— one week, I was late four times. I remember coming in one morning with two dozen donuts, hearing my boss say, "Late again, Jeffrey?"

I said, "Yes, sir."

He said, "I see you brought donuts. You should get stock in Dunkin Donuts."

I replied, "Yeah—or at least a Dunkin Donuts credit card."

Sam laughed and said, "Let's get to work."

It was a good thing that Sam liked donuts.

My next big job was my favorite—building a commercial building out of wood from the ground up, everything but the concrete. A job like this didn't come around every day. I loved working outside whenever possible, especially this time of year late in the spring when the mornings were cool and there was not a lot of rain. It was almost impossible to get bored on a job like this because there are so many different jobs to do.

We started with the layout of the building, and then we built the exterior walls. Next we would install the framing work for the roof made from factory wooden trusses. Luckily, we had a crane to help set them. The job advanced well, and around late September of that year, it was really coming together. My partner and I were given the job of installing the siding around the exterior of the building. This meant we would need to build scaffolding to get to the top of the walls.

One beautiful September morning, we set up to work on the south end of the building. This end of the building featured a very nice wooded park with many trees and lots of animals. That morning, I happened to have my buck call in my overalls, and I used it to call to some deer I had seen in the park a couple hundred yards away. I made the grunting call a few times, and my boss, Tim, came out to see what was making the noise.

He called up the scaffold to me and yelled, "What is that noise?"

I told him I was calling to some bucks in the distance. Just then, three bucks approached within twenty yards of the scaffold—two big eight points and one huge ten point. Tim took a picture of them and then said we'd better get back to work.

Later that afternoon, I fell climbing down the scaffold. I did catch myself somewhat, but not before my chest landed squarely on the top rung of the scaffold. My partner saw it happen and asked if I was all right. I told him I was fine and that it had just knocked the wind out of me. The fall hurt a little bit, but I went back to work for the rest of the day.

The next morning, it hurt really badly; I couldn't lift my arms above my chest. I called in sick that day and went to see my doctor. The doctor took x-rays, and everything seemed good. He told me that I had bruised ribs, and I should take it easy for a while, so I took his advice and had a few days off work until I could maneuver better.

The company I worked for at the time didn't hold the falling incident against me. However things were really getting worse for me. I was becoming concerned for my safety as well as others around me. I finished out that project and worked for another year or so.

I decided to consult an attorney from my union. With the advice of my doctor and attorney, along with the consent of my union, I was able to draw my pension early. I could have tried to stick it out, but I was worried, and the question of whether or not Workman's Comp would cover me at work was a very real issue. My neurologist commented, "In a way you're lucky. All those years as a carpenter with narcolepsy and you still have all your fingers."

I responded, "I guess I learned to use the saws the right way." My doctor smiled and nodded, but he was right I was lucky. That was it—my career as a carpenter was over. Ironically, the last official job I worked on was a sleep-study addition at a hospital near me.

CHAPTER 19

FREE FALLING

Retiring from being a carpenter was rough on me. I really liked my job, and it was hard to give up. About six months after giving up carpentry, I started a new medicine. At first, I thought the medicine seemed to be working pretty well. About that time, a relative asked if I could help on a roof. I thought that maybe if this worked out, I could go back to being a carpenter. I agreed, and I let the person know that I would just help out as the ground guy. This was early May, one of my favorite times to be outside in Michigan.

Like I have mentioned, I loved getting up early and starting work with the sun. I showed up at my relative's house, and a few of us got started. I was feeling good, and it didn't take long until I was on the roof. Within the first two hours, it happened: I went crashing to the ground head first onto the concrete. It seemed like slow motion to me, but I bet the whole fall took less than one second. I remember that as I fell, I could see every brick-and-mortar joint on the side of the house, almost as if they were sitting in my hand and I was looking them over with a magnifying glass. Next, I could see my left hand spread out like I was giving the concrete on the driveway a high five. I could see my finger nails on my left hand like I was getting ready to trim them. Next, my right hand shook the concrete in a much similar fashion. Then I remember turning my head away from the concrete as if to let the concrete kiss my cheek instead of my lips.

As I lay comfortably on the concrete, real time seemed to start again. The best way I can explain this is that it was like I was watching a movie, and as soon as I started to fall, someone or something pressed pause and allowed me to sit back and look at the situation and make the best adjustments to that particular part of the film so I would be able to walk away from the fall. I did a little research on this type of an event, and it seems like what was happening is something known as subjective time dilation. Apparently somehow your brain seems to process information very efficiently in these types of circumstances where your life could be in danger. It is like a super computer. Anyway, I thank God for whatever it is called—maybe a form of divine intervention.

Right after the fall, my friend and a relative came running over to the driveway side where I fell from the roof.

They didn't say anything—they seemed more shocked than I did. I remember telling them they should probably call an ambulance. Someone responded they had already done this. Just then, I remember moving my legs to see if they still worked. They did—I thought that was a good sign. I still lay on the concrete in the driveway, and everyone agreed I shouldn't try to move until the ambulance arrived. I remember thinking, *Why couldn't I have fallen on the grass side of the house?* Oh well, no matter what happened, it had happened, and it was over now.

The ambulance arrived very quickly. The paramedics approached me and asked me a few questions, like who was the president and other things like that. I must have answered them all correctly, because the paramedics were satisfied that I was coherent. I remember asking one of them, when they placed me in the ambulance, if I was going to live. The paramedic answered yes, and that was all I needed to hear.

We arrived at the hospital, and the nurses there got to working on me right away. I knew my arms were messed up, and probably my face as well. I wasn't sure of the extent of my injuries. The doctor ordered x-rays on both my arms, and a little while later, he came in my little room to consult me. The first thing he said to me was, "I see it says in your file you have narcolepsy."

I said, "Yes."

He said, "You know you can't do this kind of work."

I told him that I was aware of that, and he proceeded to tell me that I had broken both arms. Then he asked, "How are you going to wipe your butt?"

I said, "I don't know. I guess I'm stupid, but I really like being a carpenter."

Just then my sister arrived at the hospital. She walked in my room, and I gave her a big smile. She looked as white as a ghost. She said, "I can't believe you're smiling."

I said, "I am glad I still can."

I asked her how bad my face looked, knowing my face landed right on the concrete. She said it was pretty bad, especially on the right side that had hit the concrete.

My face was really torn up—I had stitches above my right eye, and when I finally looked in the mirror, it did look pretty bad. The doctor put my left arm in a cast and said I would probably need surgery on the left arm, and perhaps my right arm as well. He continued to set my right arm and sent me home with a removable cast. He also sent me home with antibiotic scripts, Vicodin, and a solution to clean my face. He told me I need to make an appointment with an orthopedic surgeon. My sister drove me home.

When I arrived home, my six-month-old Lab puppy, Hunter, came rushing to the door. He looked at me like, *What happened to you, Dad?* My face was pretty messed up.

Once home my sister cleaned my face up and gave me my prescriptions, but I wouldn't take the Vicodin. I thought that I might get addicted to it, and as someone who had been accused of being on drugs most of my life, I didn't want that to happen.

Next I remembered what the doctor said about wiping my butt. I did have a removable cast on my right arm that allowed me *some* motion when I took it off. Then, I remembered my oldest brother worked with a friend of ours who had lost both of his arms. I called my brother up and filled him in on what had happened, and I asked him to ask Gary how he wipes his butt. He asked him, and he said find a stick or something with an angle to it and try to make that work. I thanked him, and it seemed like almost right away, my dog, Hunter, came in from the backyard with the perfect stick from my maple tree. Not only did he bring me the perfect stick, but he chewed the bark off the stick. The stick almost looked like it was sanded with sand paper when Hunter gave it to me. I made that stick work until I had more use of my right arm. Dogs are awesome.

My siblings took turns coming over to help me with chores, caring for my dog, cleaning my face, and other things like that. I made an appointment with a surgeon, and he determined that I was going to need surgery on my left arm but said that the doctor in emergency did a great job setting my right arm and I would get away with just having a cast on that one. We set up a time to schedule a surgery a couple of weeks out, and then I was on my way to another doctor to check out my face and stitches over my eye.

I was very worried about my face—it honestly looked really bad. The doctor at the next appointment told me I was lucky and that I could have lost all my teeth. He also told me the skin in my face was healing really well and I may get lucky there too. He recommended that I visit a dermatologist after it healed and reminded me to clean my face twice a day. I told him I didn't want to take the Vicodin. He scolded me and told me to take it (at least when I was getting my face cleaned). He assured me that I wouldn't become addicted to it, and I agreed to take it.

A couple of days later, the crown on my bottom right molar popped out. This was the only crown I had; in fact, I had just recently had it put on. When my dentist put it in, it was way too high—almost like it wasn't even the right tooth for my mouth. I went back to her a couple of times to have it refitted, but since I had never had one before and I didn't know what it should feel like, I finally decided it was good enough.

I decided to get a new dentist to fix it now. My new dentist ended up pulling that tooth. He also found out the tooth directly above that tooth was cracked. He was able to fix that tooth. The dentist and I talked about my falling incident and how it related to my high crown, and we both agreed that it was a blessing in disguise. Had that tooth on my back molar been flush with my other teeth when I fell, all my teeth might have cracked together and I would have had way much more damage—possibly even cracking all my teeth on that side of my mouth. Crazy how things work out sometimes.

I had my surgery on my left wrist, and it worked out great. My face healed up pretty good—I can still tell what happened, but it isn't very noticeable. Within two months, I was hitting balls around my backyard to my dog, Hunter. I remember my oldest brother stopped by my house after work one day and caught me having fun. He said, "You heal fast."

I said, "Yeah, I guess I do."

That was the end of me even considering working as a carpenter.

CHAPTER 20

MORE WORKING WITH NARCOLEPSY

Once I decided carpentry was out of my future for good, I had to decide what was next for me. I asked my neurologist what I should do with the rest of my life, and he responded sleep. At the time, I had to take naps during the day, but I never imagined how bad it could get. By the time I was putting the finishing touches on this book, I was sleeping more than I was awake, and that isn't any fun. I have read about people with narcolepsy in their forties and fifties being almost bedridden—I hope that doesn't happen to me.

I had heard from a couple of people that the state and federal governments had some pretty good retraining programs for people with disabilities. I didn't really consider myself a person with a disability, but I guess I am—that is a very hard thing for me to accept. I did some investigating and signed up for one of the programs. I was excited at first. They had options for schooling and help for disabled people finding jobs that could give accommodations to them in the workplace. I thought this was a great idea. One such accommodation for a person with a sleep disorder could be scheduled nap times during the day. The government may even pay for a place for the individual to take a nap.

That all sounded quite interesting to me. I was assigned to a case worker, and we went over my options. At first, I had to take some tests to see where I may be most useful, or what type a career I would be best suited for. I scored very high on my math tests. My case worker suggested I go back to school to be a math teacher. I thought about that, but I would have to go to school full time. My doctor and I thought that would be too hard for me—especially when you consider the fact that I had to take several naps during the day.

I ended up going another route. I put my résumé together and started shopping myself around, knowing my case worker had my back with my disability and my need for accommodations. It didn't take long, and I had an interview with a major, well-known corporation. I informed my case worker about my interview and let her know I was going to need her help with my accommodations. She got upset with me right away. She told me that I shouldn't tell them about your disability or they wouldn't hire me. I told her I have to tell them—I'm going to need to take naps, and I could fall because of my cataplexy. Then, I asked her if she had even read my doctor's note. She said, "Maybe you're not ready to go to work!"

I said to her, "Why have I been wasting my time coming here if you can't help me out? I thought that was the whole point—you could stand up for me and help with my accommodation."

She didn't know what to say, or maybe, she didn't know what to do.

She informed me that maybe I could start a microbusiness so I could be my own boss and make my own hours. I said, "Okay, whatever."

My case worker proceeded to give me pamphlets on how to start my own business. Then she sent me to a business seminar that could also help me. I studied the pamphlets and went to the seminar and went back to see her to find out what next.

She then told me I had to decide what kind of a business to start and put together a plan for it. At this point, I had already spent over six months going back and forth to this government agency and still hadn't gotten any help yet. I then told her what type of business I wanted to start—a business helping handicap people get jobs. She looked at me funny; after all that was what her job was. I was totally serious, she may have thought I was being a smart-ass, but I wasn't. In the end I got nothing out of the whole experience but a hard time. Maybe they just didn't know how to help a person with a disability like mine. Maybe they were too lazy to care. It is a shame, though; at that point in my life, I may have been able to function in a good job with the right help. For the record and for whoever may need help, there is a government agency called Jobsite Assistance Network, or JAN for short. This agency has brochures for many disabilities. The brochures explain different accommodations that the government may help to pay for if a company wants to hire a person with a disability. One such brochure is one for people with sleep disorders. I did give this brochure to my case worker, but apparently she didn't have the time to read it.

CHAPTER 21

DIPLOPIA

Double vision (or diplopia, the clinical term) has been a major problem for me. I first noticed it around 2005. While reading a paper or navigating on the computer, words would begin to move on me. They would move up and down, blur together, and sometimes I would see double.

Of course, this would freak me out, and I mentioned this to my neurologist. We decided to get my eyes looked at. I made an appointment with a neural ophthalmologist. I arrived at my appointment with my new specialist and informed the doctor of my double-vision problem. The neural ophthalmologist performed many tests on me. When my appointment was over, the doctor told me I had the best vision he had ever seen and told me there was nothing wrong with my eyes. I knew I had good vision, but sometimes it was doubled. I shared my experience with my sister, and she said, "You need to see my ophthalmologist. He is the best." So I made an appointment with him. I was very surprised how quickly he could confirm my double vision. Within five minutes of performing a check-up on my eyes, he caught it. He called it an euphoria. Every time he measured my eyes, my eyes would have a slightly different euphoria. I told my new eye doctor about all the tests the neural ophthalmologist performed on me. My new eye doctor was surprised.

He said, "He didn't catch your double vision?"

I replied, "No."

He replied, "Wow, that is hard to believe."

I am not surprised one doctor found my problem so easy and the other one couldn't find it with an array of test. I have become used to meeting doctors who don't do a very good job. I will have to say my sister was right her doctor was the best eye doctor.

Now that we had determined the problem, the question was what to do about it. The Narcolepsy Network includes blurred and double vision as one of the possible symptoms of narcolepsy. Very little information on what to do about it (if anything can be done) was available to me. We decided to try glasses with prism in them to see if they could correct the problem.

I tried a prescription with prisms, but that didn't seem to work at all. We decided to increase the prism prescription, but to no avail. I did try reading with a patch over my eye, and the patch would work sometimes. When target practicing for archery, it seemed to help some. Ironically, I had way better than 20/20 vision—it was just blurred or doubled, mostly when reading or focusing on one thing, like a target. The problem with the patch was I would lose depth perception. I would also get blurred vision when using the patch, and headaches would usually follow.

What to do next? I had seen a couple of different doctors in town to see if anyone had a different idea. One suggested a surgery on the muscle of one eye. He said we could just do surgery on one eye first to see what happens, but I didn't like that idea. When I mentioned the surgery to my neurologist, he said no way—he felt it had nothing to do with my muscles in my eyes and it would just screw up my eyes even worse.

I decided to do more research on my own. I discovered an article on the Internet from the Mayo Clinic, dating back to the seventies. The researcher discovered diplopia in many of the patients with narcolepsy. In fact, he discovered that many times it would be the first symptom he would find in many of his patients with narcolepsy

I decided to make an appointment and fly out to the Mayo Clinic to see if someone in the department of neurology could help me. When I arrived at the Mayo Clinic, I had many of the same tests performed on me that I had back home.

The verdict was very similar—they gave me a prescription for glasses with prisms in them. I thanked them and headed home. These glasses did not work for me either.

On my next appointment with my neurologist, I brought my records from the Mayo Clinic. At check-in, I talked to one of the assistants in the office and handed them my records. She casually asked if the Mayo Clinic has been better than her office, and I said no. She left the room. *I wasn't going to the Mayo Clinic because I didn't think they knew what they were doing*, I thought. I was just looking for answers.

Just then, my neurologist walked in. He said, "I would be doing the same thing as you if I had narcolepsy—going everywhere I could and finding out anything I could to make my narcolepsy better." That made me feel better, and it also confirmed I was in the right doctor's office because I could tell that my doctor had my back.

I still have many problems with my vision, even to this day. In fact, it only has gotten worse. While writing this book, I used many alternative methods, like Dragon NaturallySpeaking. My eyes are really bad when I look at the computer screen. One thing is for sure—if I take a long nap before I work on the computer, my eyes do better, at least at first.

I still have never received a very good answer why I get double vision. Maybe nobody knows for sure. I think it could have something to do with my brain always trying to take me into REM, but that is just a thought. I still have better than 20/20 vision when checked periodically by optometrists. I have always had the best vision in my family. Although I still shoot archery fairly well, I used to be lights out twenty years ago. One of my brothers mentioned that maybe I have had good vision all my life because I spend so much time in REM—my eye muscles get a good work-out. I thought, *That isn't a bad theory at all. I have talked to other people with narcolepsy who experience double vision; however most of the narcoleptics I have spoken with have not experienced this symptom. Some medical professionals have mentioned diplopia could be related to cataplexy.*

CHAPTER 22

CLOUD OF SMOKE

How do you get narcolepsy? That is a good question! Much has been learned in the last fifteen to twenty years about this disease, but there is undoubtedly much more to be learned.

There have been many studies on humans and animals—most notably, dogs. In general, it has been determined approximately one in two thousand people have narcolepsy. Some say more, but most studies have concluded the one-in-two-thousand number.

Most research suggests a genetic predisposition to narcolepsy and cataplexy. This does not mean that if you have the genes associated with narcolepsy, you will have narcolepsy. Having a genetic predisposition to a disease or disorder does not give you the disease, but it means you can be more susceptible to the disease.

Regarding narcolepsy, very few people who carry the genes associated with narcolepsy will end up with the disease. This can be confusing to patients as well as the medical field. Like I mentioned in chapter 5, the genetic test should only be used to rule out narcolepsy, after all other tests have been performed. In some rare cases, a patient could have narcolepsy without carrying the genes associated with it (but this is usually not the case).

According to the Narcolepsy Network and other leading organizations, it is theorized a patient will come down with narcolepsy because of an environmental trigger or traumatic experience or sickness, usually as a child or adolescent.

How did I get narcolepsy? I do not know for sure. When you ask my family members, they say my symptoms probably started when I was four or five. I do have some theories of my own about how I have acquired narcolepsy.

While researching and writing this book, I have had many conversations with family members and medical professionals. At a recent family gathering, I was discussing the possibilities with my cousin. We talked about the environmental-trigger theory, and she reminded me of something myself and my siblings could never forget. She mentioned that my parents both smoked heavily. In my pre-elementary and early grade-school years, my family lived in a very small house in Metro Detroit. Mom, Dad, six kids, and a dog—very cramped to say the least. My father would smoke two packs of cigarettes (the unfiltered kind) each day. My mother would smoke about half of that, but the filtered kind. My cousin remembered when she would visit our quaint little house, as soon as the door would open, a cloud of smoke would come rushing out. My parents were very heavy smokers. It's amazing my cousin remembered all of that over thirty years ago as a child in the early seventies—it probably seemed crazy to her at the time. Back in the era of many smokers, our house was one of the smokiest. My siblings and I were more than likely exposed to more secondhand smoke than the average-smoking household of the time.

On a recent trip to visit an aunt on the other side of the family, I mentioned my research to her. She reminded me that my siblings and I had many childhood ear infections. My aunt thinks this could also be attributed to secondhand smoke.

One of my older brothers reminded me that in addition to our little childhood home being filled with cigarette smoke, our house was heated by an old oil burning stove. I am sure the atmosphere in the house didn't help anybody's lungs, including my brother who had asthma. Who knows what else it caused.

In addition to our smoke-filled house, my family would drive eight hours one way on summer vacations in a smoked-filled station wagon. Try to imagine my family's car ride: six kids, two parents, and a dog in a station wagon puffing down the highway like a magic dragon, eight hours each way.

You do not have to be Einstein to draw the conclusion that if narcolepsy is indeed set off by an environmental trigger, I found my smoking gun. I know smoking and secondhand smoke gets blamed for a lot of things, and it should. One thing my parents did was cure me from ever wanting to try smoking cigarettes.

My oldest brother and both of my parents all had lung cancer. My mother died at age fifty-seven from lung cancer. My father's lung cancer was caught in time, but he ended up with COPD and passed away at seventy-two. Billy, my brother who otherwise was a healthy, strong man, came down with lung cancer and passed away at age fifty.

Smoking and secondhand smoke get blamed for a lot of things. I don't know what caused my narcolepsy, and I may never know. I don't know what causes anybody's narcolepsy, but hopefully one day, we will have more answers. Hopefully researchers will take a look at smoking and secondhand smoke as a possibility for some of the cases of narcolepsy.

CHAPTER 23

TRAUMATIC EXPERIENCE

When I was three years old, I shared a bedroom with my three older brothers. Looking back, that seems crowded, but we never felt that way—it was just the norm to us. I shared a bed with my older brother next in age from me. I have recently shared this story with two of my older siblings. When relaying the story to my older brother, he stopped me and said, "You remember when you were three years old?"

I replied, "Yes, as a matter of fact, it is one of the most vivid memories—if not the most vivid—in my life."

One evening, after our parents tucked all us kids in bed, my mother and father retired to the living room, as they so often did to watch television. We lived in a small three-bedroom house. The boys' room was at the end of the house next to the bathroom. The living room was straight up the hallway from the bathroom at the front of the house.

My father was a drinker—he would drink beer almost every night of my childhood. As I mentioned, I was three years old, and I was off diapers and thought to be pretty much potty trained. On this night, not too long after I fell asleep, I suddenly awoke. I was definitely wet, and I was scared because my father had warned me not to wet my bed again.

At this time, I crawled out of bed and snuck my way into the bathroom. I could hear my father's footsteps coming down the hallway. I tried to hide my wet clothes, but it was too late. My father stood over me, his booming voice like thunder, and asked, "What did you do—wet your bed again?!"

I was shaking and very scared. At that moment my father bent me over the bathtub. I can still hear my mother's voice from the living room, still ringing in my ears to this day.

"Billy! (my father's name) No!"

My father spanked me, if you want to call it that—he hit me as hard as he could, and I bet more than ten times. I thought I was going to die. Every lash my father inflicted on me felt like the end of the world over and over again. I have never felt such terror again at any point in my life.

My father was a construction worker and a drinker. That is no excuse, but I am sure the alcohol didn't help the situation. I never wet my bed again—my father fixed me of that. To this day, I can travel many, many hours without having to use a bathroom. I don't know if this was the trigger that set off my narcolepsy or not. I do know from my memory and my older siblings memories that when I was three or four years old, many of my narcolepsy symptoms, especially my automatic behavior, started to manifest themselves.

I really liked my dad—in fact, he was one of my favorite people ever. Most people liked my dad. If he was in a room with twenty people, there would be a couple of people who wouldn't like him, a couple of people who could take him or leave him, but most people would really like him. Most people would have a lot of fun hanging out with him. When writing this chapter, I am fighting back tears—I seriously thought about not telling this part of the story. I discussed it with a few people close to me, and we decided I had too. My father wasn't as bad as the worst thing he had done in his life, but he was as good as the best things he did. I hope after I leave this world, if I am thought of, people will think the same of me. I love you, Dad.

I don't know if secondhand smoke, my whipping experience, or another virus or sickness was the trigger that set off my narcolepsy. I don't know if I was born with it. It may be something else. I may never know. Deep in my heart, if you put each possibility in a suitcase and play the game show Deal or No Deal with them, I have to pick the suitcase with the whipping I took as a three-year-old. I really did think I was going to die that evening.

My thoughts about how I ended up with narcolepsy, after my life living with it and the past ten years of learning about it, I believe I went through a very bad experience. Whether it be environmental or something else, I think my brain did something to save itself (and in turn, me). I think somehow it destroyed or started to destroy the orexin in my system and other parts of my brain. My brain and my genetic makeup may have saved me from something far worse—God forbid, maybe even death. The brain is very complex, and it can do amazing things. The genetic predisposition to narcolepsy may not be 100 percent, but what if the people who carry the genes associated with narcolepsy and cataplexy possess a genetic ability to destroy part of the brain to prevent death? What if in some cases one event sets off narcolepsy and another event sets off cataplexy? Narcolepsy may be autoimmune. Researchers are still investigating that possibility.

CHAPTER 24

HUNTER BEAR

In early spring 2007, about two years after I was diagnosed with narcolepsy, I decided to look into getting a dog. I had a dog my whole childhood, but this would be my first dog as an adult. I decided to check online to begin my search. I was pretty sure I wanted a Lab-type dog, and that was where I began my search.

The first dog I looked at was a four-month-old Lab–Cocker Spaniel mix. He was a hyper little thing like you might expect; he had a very unique look to him. I liked him right away. The family who owned him had another dog, but this one was an adult. I asked why they wanted to get rid of the puppy, and they told me that having the two dogs was too much work for them. I played with the puppy for a while and told the family I had a few more dogs to look at. I really liked this dog, but I knew I should look at a few more.

The next evening I headed toward Ypsilanti, about an hour drive from my house near Detroit. I spoke to a lady who rescues dogs over there. She told me she had two really nice puppies of German shepherd–Labrador mix. They sounded great, but I was about half way there when I realized I could not get the other puppy out of my mind. There was something really cool about him. I phoned the lady and told her my thoughts. She advised me that I should go get that puppy right away if he was still available. I thanked her and proceeded to call the family with the Lab–Cocker Spaniel mix. They told me he was still available. I hurried over to claim him.

My new dog and I had a lot in common—even more than I knew at the time. Having a dog of my own was new to me and would take a little getting used to. As soon as my new dog entered my house, he marked his new territory on the floor right away. He was already potty trained for the most part, and he didn't do that again.

I tried giving my dog a name that would fit. After trying a few different names that didn't seem to stick, I settled on Hunter. This was the perfect name for my new family member. Later, Hunter's name was modified to Hunter Bear— this was because he resembled a little black bear.

Hunter Bear and I had a blast together, and soon, he went everywhere I went. It wasn't long until Hunter Bear was helping me with my narcolepsy and cataplexy. In the evenings, I would take a medicine called Xyrem—this medicine had to be taken in two doses. I had to take the first dose just before I fell asleep, and the next dose would come four hours later. This meant I would have to set an alarm to take the second dose about four hours later. I could never hear the alarm for the second dose because I sleep very heavily. Almost as soon as I got him, Hunter Bear recognized this. It didn't take long, and he was right there licking my face to wake me up each night for the second dose.

Hunter Bear provided me with much more help with my narcolepsy and cataplexy. Like I mentioned, Hunter Bear went everywhere with me—this was a great asset for me, especially while driving. Hunter Bear would stay totally alert sitting in the passenger seat just like a human—in fact, you might take a double check while driving past just to be sure. He would inform me with a unique barking sound when he thought I was getting tired. At first, I didn't understand what he was trying to tell me, but I figured it out quite soon. He became an alarm clock for me while driving, letting me know before I knew I was getting tired.

Hunter Bear soon learned to be able to inform if I was going to have a cataplexy experience. Stress sets off my cataplexy, among other things. Hunter Bear would come to me and let me know it was time to settle down or take a nap. At this time in my life, I caved in to taking naps during the day—I had to, or I couldn't function at all.

I shared my experiences I had with Hunter Bear with my family and friends. Most of them thought it was cool. Others thought I was making this up. Around 2015, a dog trainer in Seattle, Washington, started training dogs for people with narcolepsy. I guess Hunter Bear was a little before his time. Dogs are really smart, and they sense things we could never dream of.

I lost Hunter Bear on March 28, 2011—that was the day he passed away. My wife at the time and I got another dog within a week. I missed Hunter Bear very much. Our new dog, Gunner, a Lab-beagle mix, helped me well with a few of the things Hunter Bear could do. He would wake me up for my second dose of Xyrem in much the same fashion as Hunter Bear; he would also let me know when to take naps. He did fall short when it came to the driving part. He would tend to fall asleep, not all the time but enough where he could not be my crutch while driving.

My ex-wife ended up with Gunner. I am still trying to find another dog like Hunter Bear—I miss you, buddy.

In September 2015, my then two-year-old daughter, we will call her Adelle, and I decided to get our own dog, this time a Lab-retriever mix. Adelle picked her out, the only girl of the litter. My daughter named her Minnie, after, you guessed it, Minnie Mouse. Our new pup was only two months old, and she would need a lot of training.

Minnie was definitely the most hyper dog I had ever known, and maybe the fastest. Minnie has been clearing my fences like a deer in one leap since she was four months old. I have privacy fences now, but if she wants to, she can get over them. In fact, a kennel I board her at keeps her on a leash when she goes outside because she cleared one of their six-foot privacy fences.

Minnie is currently two years old. Same thing with her: when it comes to waking me up for my second dose of Xyrem, a big lick on the face and I am up. It must be like the Pavlov's dogs thing when they hear the alarm. Minnie is really good driving with me—she never falls asleep. Minnie is not as good as Hunter Bear was in the whole letting me know when to take naps drill, but she is young.

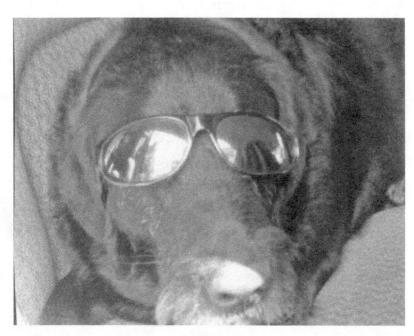

Hunter Bear Styling

CHAPTER 25

REM AWAKENING

One of the symptoms of narcolepsy is hallucinations. This requires a little bit of explanation to help define what is meant by hallucinations in narcoleptic patients. For myself and others I have talked to, hallucinations occur on occasion—usually when waking up from a dream. What happens to me is, I will suddenly wake up in the middle of a dream, I will open my eyes, but the dream will continue in my mind. This only last for a few seconds. This is technically considered a hallucination, but in this instance it can also be called a REM awakening. Sometimes, as reported by friends and family members, I will wake up screaming. This can be very scary for someone who has never seen this before as well as the person waking up.

Although my hallucinations will occur mostly when I am waking from a dream, this can be dangerous. An example, this has happened on many occasions while falling asleep as a passenger in an automobile. I fall asleep very easily as a passenger in a car. When going on trips of an hour or more, sometimes I will wake from just such a dream. Very often, I will lunge for the steering wheel. Some of my relatives and friends have seen this many times. Luckily, nothing bad has ever occurred from this. This type of an event while driving with others has been noticed on occasions since my late teens—well over twenty years before I was diagnosed with narcolepsy.

When most people hear the word "hallucination," it obviously freaks them out. It is important to note that not all narcoleptics get these hallucinations. I wish there was a better word to use in place of "hallucinations," because when most people hear it, they definitely think the worst. Many people will assume you go through the day imagining things, but in this instance, that is not the case. Ironically my brother who witnessed this many times would quite often say, "You're hallucinating again!"

I would think he was being mean, but he was actually right. This was many years before I was diagnosed with narcolepsy. When you look back at all my symptoms that were present at an early age, it is amazing to think I wasn't diagnosed with narcolepsy or even something else many years before I was.

CHAPTER 26

PARENTING WITH NARCOLEPSY

P arenting is its own science that is ever-evolving, and it is different from person to person, family to family, and decade to decade. There is no right or wrong way to parent—one can only hope to do his or her best and hope for the best possible outcome. A parent can take parenting classes, accept advice from friends and family members, and, today, even google how to parent. I took a parenting class, and I recommend it to everyone. I learned a lot from my parenting class.

Parenting comes down to a lot of hard work, a never-say-die attitude, and mutual respect between the parents and children. It is not the parents' responsibility to control their children, as much as it is to teach the children to control themselves. Parenting is a challenge for anyone. It can be even more challenging if you have a disability.

Parenting for me has been a challenge—not only to parent but also to keep the right to parent. One of the reasons I decided to write this book was to inform the average person about narcolepsy—what it is and what it isn't. This is very important when you have to deal with the court systems. My experience in hiring attorneys has been grave at best. I was lucky if my attorney googled a bad definition of narcolepsy. My divorce and custody battle is a prime example of this injustice.

If you are in a wheel chair, other people can see you are in a wheel chair. They may not know why, but they can usually understand why given a proper explanation. Having narcolepsy and cataplexy is not that easy to explain, especially if the people you are explaining it to don't care or maybe don't believe it. Some people may even try to use it against an individual with narcolepsy. I know that is hard to believe, but people with disabilities are taken advantage of from time to time.

During my divorce proceedings, it was suggested that I may not have joint custody granted to me because I have narcolepsy. In fact, it was suggested that I have no overnights with my daughter. I was totally shocked, to say the least. During my marriage, there was never a thought of such restrictions. Less than six months before my divorce papers were filed, not only did my seventeen-month-old daughter spend the night alone with me, but her six-year-old cousin also spent the night with me. Their mothers went out to a reunion and were quite happy to have me watch the children. The kids had a blast hanging out with me—most kids do. Of course, the night went perfectly, and both mothers thanked me in the morning. I hugged my niece goodbye, and that was the end of it.

The funny thing is nighttime is the best time for me—if I have any issues with my narcolepsy or cataplexy, it would be during the day. You can understand my dismay to my all-of-a-sudden new restrictions to my parenting.

As soon as my older brother found out I was fighting for joint custody of my daughter and he heard maybe I couldn't parent well because of my narcolepsy, he was outraged to say the least. My brother stated this in a phone conversation with me at the time: "You have to be kidding me, Jeffy. You were like Tony Danza to your family."

My brother was referring to Tony Danza who played Tony, a housekeeper in the sitcom *Who's the Boss*.[4] We both laughed hard, but he was right. I did many things for my family before and during my marriage that were similar to the sitcom, like cooking, shopping, and laundry. Honestly, I am a very good dad, and I would never let my little–sweet pea Adelle fall into harm's way. It pissed me off, to say the least.

---

4 *Who's the Boss*, created by Martin Cohan and Blake Hunter, aired on ABC Television, 1984–1992.

If you have ever had to hire an attorney on the fly, you know it can be challenging. As soon as my ex-wife filed for divorce, all I could think of was I can't let my daughter out of my sight. I don't know all the legal aspects in child custody, but I knew it would be advantageous for me to make sure my daughter lived with me until the divorce was final. My sister helped me find an attorney, and whenever I had to meet with the attorney, my sister would leave work to watch my daughter for me. Thank God I had my sister to count on, or I could have been in even worse of a nightmare.

My first-divorce attorney kept me in the dark about everything. She, my attorney led me to believe I might lose my fight for joint custody even though my doctor, a well-known neurologist with unheralded experience with narcolepsy, wrote letters in complete support of me and my parenting skills. After consulting with a relative who was himself in the legal field, we both agreed that I needed a better attorney who could consult with me better. I fired my first attorney and then hired a new one. This attorney was better and assured me that just the fact that I have narcolepsy would not stop me from being a good parent. After much more time and attorney fees, I won my right to have joint custody of my daughter. Although my new attorney was much better than my first one, he allowed some restrictions to my medicine and other things that I reluctantly agreed to before I ran out of money.

During my custody battle, I searched for advice from attorneys as well as other people. I tried to find somebody who was going through a similar situation as I was. I also looked for narcolepsy support groups in my area, but I found none. I am currently trying to start one in Southeast Michigan.

Parenting with narcolepsy can be challenging—I have learned that when possible, you should share as much information as you can with your child. At present, my biological daughter is five. She is a trooper and very smart. I have all the symptoms of narcolepsy and cataplexy; some of them can seem quite odd and hard to explain to a normal person. I am truly blessed with my daughter. She understands my narcolepsy as well as or better than most people I have tried to enlighten.

One symptom, daytime sleepiness, is the easiest to explain. Adelle understands that I have to sleep more than most people. She understands that sometimes I have a babysitter watch her while I take naps. My daughter is very caring; she asks me on a daily basis if I am tired or need to lie down. If I am changing a light bulb, she will rush over to hold my legs when I am on a chair. I totally love her, and I am totally lucky to say the least.

A harder symptom to understand is cataplexy—cataplexy shows up in many ways. One form of cataplexy that happens a lot to me is I drop things. Every day I drop multiple objects. This can look like I am totally uncoordinated or even drunk. My daughter knows not to worry, and that it is just part of Dad's cataplexy. I also can start to slur my words, and sometimes, this is very noticeable—Adelle will say if someone notices, "Don't worry, that is just Daddy's narcolepsy." This next symptom is one of the hardest to deal with for me and can be quite embarrassing. I sometimes frown. One time, my daughter saw this symptom and said, "Daddy, are you okay, or are you sad?"

I said, "No, honey. I'm frowning because of my narcolepsy and cataplexy."

I sometimes lose the muscle tone in my face, and it makes me look like I'm frowning. I told her not to worry—I am smiling on the inside. Since then, if Adelle sees this occurring, she will say to whoever might also notice this occur, "Don't worry, that is just Daddy's narcolepsy—he is smiling on the inside."

Another symptom that my daughter picks up all the time is when I just stare off. She is really good at spotting this, and she will let me know right away. And I will snap out of it. Now that I am a parent with narcolepsy (and a single parent to boot), I am really searching out support. This is sometimes hard to find. For example, I need affordable babysitters who are dependable. This year, I gave in to hiring a lawn service so I can spend more of my waking hours with my daughter. I don't know what the future holds, but hopefully, I will be able to be the best parent I can be for my daughter. I do wish there were more resources for parents with narcolepsy and other disabilities.

I would like to share a story from this past Easter. I was getting Adelle ready to spend the night and holiday at her mother's. I have mentioned before that I have a hard time keeping track of things. On this occasion, Adelle was all packed up and ready to go. Just then, I was looking all over the place for my car keys. I spent a good fifteen minutes looking for them. Finally, I gave in and decided to grab my extra set of keys I keep hanging up in the kitchen. I strapped Adelle into her car seat and proceeded to my position in the driver's seat. Adelle knew I was looking for my keys. Just before I pulled out of my driveway, I mentioned one more time that I wished I knew where my car keys were. Adelle heard me and said, "Dad, April fools!"

I said, "What?"

She then said, "Dad, don't be mad at me. I never played a prank before."

I responded, "What are you talking about?"

She responded, "I put your keys under your pillow for an April fool's joke."

The next day was April 1. I looked at her and said, "Really, please don't do that again."

She responded, "Okay, Dad."

I told her that it was pretty funny, but next time she wanted to play an April fool's joke, she should make sure it doesn't involve something so important.

"Okay, Dad," she replied. "Sure you're not mad at me?"

I told Adelle, "How could I be mad at you? You're so cute that if you were a chocolate bunny, I would eat you all up."

We both laughed—after all tomorrow was Easter Sunday.

Adelle loves going to carnivals, and I love taking her. Recently, before this book was published, Adelle and I visited a carnival two days in a row. We had a blast, and needless to say, Adelle wore me out—but not until I won her some cool prizes. We had about a one-mile drive back home after the carnival. Adelle and I headed back to our truck, and I buckled her in. I told Adelle, "Boy, am I glad we don't have far to drive home tonight."

Then I asked her, "When you get older, are you going to drive me around?"

Adelle responded, "Sure, unless I have narcolepsy, then we are out of luck."

She is so funny. Sometimes I think she is much older than her age would suggest.

Adelle and her daddy on her favorite ride, the Ferris wheel,
at age two and a half

CHAPTER 27

THE TRUTH

My father would always say "things aren't always as they seem"—maybe you have heard this too. That is ever so true in regards to my life with narcolepsy. Not only was it a long journey just to find out I had a condition called narcolepsy, but trying to explain to the general population what narcolepsy is and how it affects a person isn't just difficult for me—it is even hard for organizations like the Narcolepsy Network to get the message out. This reminds me of an article from the quarterly magazine put out by the foundation.

A young child was diagnosed with narcolepsy, had a note from her doctor, and was trying to get a nap-time accommodation at her school. The principal gave her a hard time and told her she should see a psychiatrist. The Narcolepsy

Network found out about this, and they flew in to visit this school district to set them straight. Since when can a principal run roughshod over a child with a doctor's note? It really is unbelievable.

Many things are hard to explain, but once you have the right information, it usually gets easier. In time things can change; what we once thought was true can totally change over time. Sometimes, even to the opposite of what was once thought to be fact can be true. It is hard to believe that at one time, some people were sure the earth was flat. In the 1940s and 1950s, lobotomies were thought to be a good last resort for people with severe mental problems. When I was growing up, Pluto was a planet. Then, one day, a bunch of scientists got together and voted Pluto off planet status. Pluto is still part of our solar system, but it is now viewed differently than a planet. The point is there are many things that we view as fact today, that ten or twenty years from now we may be saying "what were we thinking?" Some people won't believe something unless they can see it. If a person is missing a limb such as an arm or a leg, you can see it. That is the old saying "Seeing is believing." With narcolepsy you can't really see it, so some people can't believe it.

One day I wrote a little saying about the truth and what it means to me. It seems to fit in regards to many subjects, but certainly in the case of narcolepsy, it rings true.

The Truth
The Truth always is,
Always was,
And always will be.
Perceptions change.
Laws change.
Evidence changes.
Facts can change.
The Truth never changes; it always stays the same.
The Truth is in your heart; you can't see it or hold it.
But you know it is there.
You can deny the Truth,
But the Truth doesn't go away.
The Truth cannot be proven, nor disproven.
The Truth cannot be bought, nor sold.
The Truth cannot be given, nor stolen.
The Truth is always the same and always will remain.
And that's the Truth.

Jeff Wood, PWN

CHAPTER 28

MY THOUGHTS

Much of what we now know about narcolepsy has been learned with the help of Dobermans and Labrador Retrievers. These canines are known to have narcolepsy and cataplexy in high numbers. The research I have done suggests that they are the only canines to suffer from narcolepsy, as well as some poodles. Stanford University Center for Narcolepsy and Dr. Emmanuel Mignot have been at the forefront of most of this research.[5] Researchers seem to learn a lot from animals for obvious reasons. They are much easier to perform tests on than humans—animals can't say no.

I have always been fascinated by black bears—they are very interesting animals. In a way, black bears are the

---

5 "Dr. Emmanuel Mignot," Stanford Medicine, accessed October 30, 2018, https://med.stanford.edu/narcolepsy/mignot.html.

masters of sleep. I do not know if there are many studies on black bears in regards to sleep, but they hibernate on average three to four months a year. I would be interested to know if they have similar levels of hypocretin as humans. Maybe they increase and decrease these levels naturally while hibernating. An interesting fact about black bears is that they are the only animals that are known to have the ability to delay implantation of the female's fertilized egg to the uterus. Black bears usually mate in June, but the fertilized egg doesn't make its way to the uterus until sometime in November. This is the black bears' natural way of preventing the fetus to develop unless the mother has enough body fat and other nutrients to survive the winter and provide milk for her cubs. Black bears may have other unique traits that we don't know about that helps them to hibernate.

Maybe research could be done on black bears to help us learn more about many sleep disorders.

One medicine I take for narcolepsy is Xyrem. One thing Xyrem does is keep me from going into REM right away when falling asleep. I take this medicine in two doses, one just before falling asleep and one about four hours later. I have noticed that many times after taking my first dose, I cannot fall asleep right away. In fact, many times I feel more awake than I do all day long. I have noticed that at this time my diplopia (double vision) seems to fade away after taking the first dose of this medicine, and it is a good time for me to read and do my bills online (at least for the first twenty minutes after taking my first dose).

Maybe Xyrem can be taken during the day in smaller doses to help some narcoleptic patients to stay awake. One way this theory can be tested on some narcoleptic patients who have double vision like myself would be to have an optometrist or ophthalmologist to observe the patients' eyes before taking a smaller dose of Xyrem. Then, about ten minutes after taking a dose of Xyrem, check the patient's eyes to see if the double vision has subsided. This idea isn't that crazy when you think about it. Xyrem would make normal people go into a deep sleep, but narcoleptic patients go into REM usually very quickly when falling asleep. One of the purposes of Xyrem is to cut down the amount of REM sleep a patient with narcolepsy has at night. So, in a way, when narcoleptics take Xyrem, they fall into a less deep sleep than they would without taking Xyrem. In my theory, after a patient like myself takes Xyrem, they are actually being pulled out of REM and becoming more alert.

Another way to test my theory would be to have twenty-or-so known narcoleptic patients to spend a few days at a sleep clinic. The narcoleptic patients in this study could all undergo an MSLT daytime sleep test without taking any medicine to see how quick they fall into REM sleep. Then, the next day they could take a small dose of Xyrem and try the MSLT test again to see whether or not they fall into REM quickly.

ADHD patients take Adderall and other medicines to help them become more focused or slowed down. The amphetamine they take would make most people very hyper or alert, but it works the opposite way on ADHD patients than it does on people without ADHD. I believe Xyrem can work much the same way in narcoleptic patients.

I have to mention this because it has bothered me ever since I read about it—I have seen many articles that suggest in the island country of Japan, one in every five hundred people have narcolepsy. This is four times the prevalence as most of the rest of the world. I can't help but think that if an environmental trigger sets off narcolepsy in many people who have narcolepsy, does this point to the long-lasting effects of the atomic bombs that were dropped on Hiroshima and Nagasaki?

CHAPTER 29

MY NARCOLEPSY

My narcolepsy has progressed throughout my life. The following is a chart that shows how much time I have spent sleeping throughout my adult years:

Hours of sleep per day	8	9	9.5	10.5	12	14
Age of sleeper	20	30	35	40	45	50

In my teens, my first signs of major cataplexy showed up. These cataplexy experiences were triggered by extreme laughter and extreme anxiety. These cataplexy occurrences would occur occasionally and would continue at about the same rate of prevalence throughout my life to current day. However, other cataplexy experiences that seem to be non-triggered have escalated throughout my life. These include loss of muscle tone in my hands that result in dropping of

Jeffrey J. Wood

many things—at this point in my life, at age fifty, this occurs daily and several times a day. I also frown throughout the day unknowingly—this is also thought to be a form of cataplexy. Slurring my speech is also an everyday occurrence and seems only to become more prevalent as I age.

At this time in my life, I am sleeping an average of fourteen hours in a twenty-four-hour time span. Driving for me has become limited, and I do not drive long distances. I know there is a great possibility that at some point in the future, I will not drive at all, and that is scary.

My double vision shows no signs of lessening and may be getting worse. I take various medications for narcolepsy and cataplexy, but none seem to work well. I may decide at some point to stop using medication all together. I have tried various therapies and have showed up for many drug trials, but none have done the trick for me yet. I recently have tried vitamin C infusions, and I am still experimenting with them. A few years ago, I was in a drug trial where the patients would consume a form of histamine. This makes sense: if antihistamine makes you tired, histamine will wake you up. I never actually got to try the drug in the trial. By the time I made it through the screening process, the trial was halted. There were too many side effects.

I exercise every day and eat extremely well. I do not drink alcohol, and I do my best to stay in the best shape possible. This may not do much for my narcolepsy, but it should help with any other health problems in much the same way as exercises I do for herniated discs I have in my back. The exercises for my back won't make my herniated discs go away, but it will strengthen all my muscles in the area to help with the burden the herniated discs put on my lower back.

Like I mentioned, I have tried many drugs and therapies for my narcolepsy—one thing I believe that gives me my best alertness is coffee and the caffeine I get from it. I know it gets me going in the morning. This brings me to another problem. Since the age of forty-five, I have been getting a lot of heavy pain from time to time in my personal area. I consulted my doctor who checked me out, and he could not find any abnormality. We discussed the possibilities of my lower back pain causing this, but it wasn't likely. We decided to make an appointment with an urologist. The urologist ran a few tests; all of them looked well. Then my urologist suggested that a lot of men who drink a lot of caffeine get this type of pain from time to time. He asked if I drink much coffee; I said yes. He suggested I stop drinking coffee and see what happens. I did try to, but I really need coffee to get me going. I thought, *I knew narcolepsy was a pain in the balls, but really?* I am still trying to find an answer for the pain problem—it isn't every day, but when I do feel it, the pain is pretty extreme.

Trying to explain narcolepsy is hard, but let me tell you, it is not just being a little tired.

In the mornings when I wake up, many times I feel like I have an extreme hangover such as one might get from drinking too much alcohol the night before. However, I would not be drinking the night before. When explaining this to a good friend of mine, he said, "It is like you get the hangover without the buzz."

That is a good way to put it.

Other times, I wake up in the morning, and my legs are totally worn out—it feels like I have been running for miles. During the day, when I am awake, I do not have total energy. I usually have a few good hours where I feel like I can do anything, but I need to be careful, especially mentally, because this feeling fades quickly and I need to be ready for it.

Sleep deprivation is used as a form of torture—obviously, I have no idea what that is like. I would have to guess it is extremely bad. The tiredness a narcoleptic person can go through is extremely bad for a lot of narcoleptics, some more than myself. It is important for me to drive home the fact that narcolepsy is nothing like being a little tired. If you know someone with narcolepsy, I hope you understand what I am trying to say.

One thing I love more than anything is music and going to concerts. In my twenties and thirties, it would not be uncommon for me to attend fifty to one hundred concerts within the span of one year. Once I hit my forties, I was lucky if I attended five concerts a year. I have played bass guitar and sang in a local rock band since the early 1990s. Since age forty, this has become much harder to the point I don't play the bar scene any more. At this point in my life,

I still play music and write songs, but it is more confined to the studio and daytime gigs. When rehearsing with my band, I am usually done by 9:00 p.m.

I don't know what the future holds, but I will never give up fighting narcolepsy or looking for ways to find more energy to do things like music. In a recent conversation with a friend of mine, I had mentioned I sleep fourteen hours a day. He said, "Wow, your days must go by fast." I told him that they do, and it sucks. Mentally, I know I can only do so much in a day, but my heart wants to do more.

Narcolepsy is totally opposite of who I am. My sister recently said to me, "Jeff, you're doing good. You are the most ambitious person I know."

I said, "Thanks for noticing."

CHAPTER 30

PORTLAND

I have learned a lot while writing this book. From the time I first thought about writing this book to the present day, I have lost a brother: Billy Wood. I lost a son, Jeffrey Stephen Wood. I lost my little buddy, my Spanador Hunter Bear. I have been married and divorced. For many different reasons, I have started and stopped writing this book. Whether this book is good or bad or somewhere in between, I needed to finish it. If for no other reason, it will put closure to a lot of things for me. In a way, it is a healing experience for me. At this point in my life, I sleep more than I am awake. My double vision has become a huge problem, especially when trying to work on a computer. I tell people I have on average about four good hours each day to get anything done. When I finish this book, I am going to spend most of those good hours, God willing, writing songs—something I love and I am good at.

I have attended the last two Narcolepsy Network annual conferences. I suggest anyone with narcolepsy try to attend at least one. The first thing I learned at the conference was that they always have an area to sleep. I thought this was awesome because I had been wondering how I could last all the way through a conference. There are a lot of things to do there—you won't be able to do it all. I met other people with narcolepsy, PWN for short. This was the first place I was able to talk in person to other people with narcolepsy and cataplexy. I made a lot of friends there and shared a lot of experiences. Thank you, Narcolepsy Network.

Mandy, a lady with narcolepsy I met at the Portland Oregon conference, exchanged narcoleptic stories with me. I mentioned to her I have two cell phones. I keep an extra one in a safe place so I can call the other phone when I lose that one. She thought that was funny and a good idea; she mentioned she would lose her phone a lot also. One evening I met Mandy to go on a small tour of Portland. I stopped buy her room to pick her up. She was ready to go, but she had misplaced a few things.

Mandy mentioned to me, "I will be ready in a minute. I just need to find my keys and a few things."

I responded, "Okay, no problem."

Mandy proceeded to tear her hotel room apart, looking for her possessions.

After about five minutes, Mandy appeared a little upset and said to me, "I'm sorry, you can go without me if you want."

I started to laugh.

Mandy exclaimed, "Why are you laughing?"

I told her, "I am not laughing at you. I am laughing with you."

She responded, "What?"

I then said, "Watching you look for your keys and things is like looking in a mirror for me; it is a healing experience."

I then told her, "Take as long as you need. I am not in a hurry."

She said, "Thanks."

I then told her, "You never have to apologize for being narcoleptic to me."

She seemed to like that. It wasn't much longer, and Mandy found her keys. And we were on our way to check out Portland.

Just before the 2017 conference in Portland, I was almost done with my book. I know I will never run out of material for this book. I am sure I will have many more narcolepsy stories in my life to share. I remember what my father used to say—"Do something, even if it's wrong."

I think what he meant was that sometimes you just have to do something and see how it works out. You can't be afraid to fail, or you will never succeed. I can't wait to be done with this book. I was totally wiped out (even more than usual) at the conclusion of the last conference in Portland, Oregon. I had to rush home and take my daughter trick or treating for Halloween. After that, I was going to finish my book as soon as possible.

At the conference, I picked up a book called *Forty Winks*, by Brenda A. Moore. This is a book about narcolepsy and dreams. I had the book with me when I boarded the plane from Portland, Oregon, to Detroit, Michigan. The flight to Detroit would take about three hours. My seat was the very last row of the airplane. I did, however, have the aisle seat. I boarded, tucked my luggage overhead, buckled up, and tried to get comfortable. I pulled out the book and opened to the first page. That was the last thing I remembered until we landed in Detroit—I must have passed right out. It seemed to be a rough landing, not too bad but I don't really know—I don't fly that much. It did seem like we hit pretty good, but like I said, I was in the back of the plane.

I woke up right away. Just then, the gentlemen in the aisle across from me was trying to get my attention. He said, "Hey buddy, was that your book?"

I said, "What?"

He said, "Was that your book in the aisle?"

I said, "I don't know—I guess so."

He said, "You should have seen it. It was on the floor, and it sailed a million miles per hour all the way to the cockpit."

I said, "Really?"

He said, "Yeah!"

I said, "Wow!"

He said, "Yeah."

Just then, the pilot came on the intercom and said, "Whoever's book that is that flew up here, I have it here on my lap."

ACKNOWLEDGMENTS

I would like to thank the following people and organizations for all their help and support:

The Narcolepsy Network, the National Organization for Rare Diseases [N.O.R.D.], the National Institute of Health, the Mayo Clinic, Caring Voice Coalition, Dr. Narayan P. Verma and the BG Tri County Sleep Clinic, Dr. Robert B. Popovski and the staff at Roseville Family Physicians, Dr. David Lustig, Dr. Charles R. Stern, Dr. Lawrence Konst, Dr. Ronald Heitman, Dr. Piero A. Simone, the Narrow Path Christian Biker Church, Fort Wayne Neurology, the Michigan Regional Council of Carpenters, Carpenters Local 687, Nicole Jeray and Swinging for Sleep, Joyce A. Scannell, and all my family and friends who have been there for me and you know who you are.

ABOUT THE AUTHOR

Jeffrey J. Wood is a (graduate apprentice) Journeyman Union carpenter with more than thirty years of experience and has lived in Metro Detroit all his life. He is also a founding member of the Detroit rock band Modern Vagrant and is a proud PWN.

GLOSSARY

Cataplexy   A sudden involuntary loss of muscle tone
               sometimes brought on by strong emotions.

Diplopia   A disorder of vision in which two images
               of a single object are seen.

Hypocretin   Either of two neuropeptides (hypocretin
               1 and hypocretin 2) that are produced
               in the hypothalamus and play a role in
               wakefulness and food intake. Also called
               orexin A and orexin B.

Hypothalamus   A region of the forebrain below the thala-
               mus that coordinates both the autonomic
               nervous system and the activity of the
               pituitary, controlling body temperature,
               thirst, hunger, and other homeostatic

	systems, and is involved in sleep and emotional activity.
Lucid dreaming	A dream where the person dreaming is aware he or she is dreaming and that he or she can control the dream to some extent.
Narcolepsy	A neurological disorder that effects the control of sleep and wakefulness, characterized by excessive daytime sleepiness.
Orexin	Either of two neuropeptides (orexin A and orexin B) that are produced in the hypothalamus and play a role in wakefulness and food intake. Also called hypocretin 1 and hypocretin 2.
Sleep paralysis	A feeling of being conscious but unable to move, occurring when the person transitions from sleep to wakefulness.

CPSIA information can be obtained
at www.ICGtesting.com
Printed in the USA
BVHW031930010520
579060BV00002B/531